INDIANS

POCAHONTAS, *Seymour*
SACAGAWEA, *Seymour*
SEQUOYAH, *Snow*
SITTING BULL, *Stevenson*
SQUANTO, *Stevenson*
TECUMSEH, *Stevenson*

NAVAL HEROES

DAVID FARRAGUT, *Long*
GEORGE DEWEY, *Long*
JOHN PAUL JONES, *Snow*
MATTHEW CALBRAITH PERRY, *Scharbach*
OLIVER HAZARD PERRY, *Long*
RAPHAEL SEMMES, *Snow*
STEPHEN DECATUR, *Smith*

NOTED WIVES and MOTHERS

ABIGAIL ADAMS, *Wagoner*
DOLLY MADISON, *Monsell*
JESSIE FREMONT, *Wagoner*
MARTHA WASHINGTON, *Wagoner*
MARY TODD LINCOLN, *Wilkie*
NANCY HANKS, *Stevenson*
RACHEL JACKSON, *Govan*

SCIENTISTS and INVENTORS

ALBERT EINSTEIN, *Hammontree*
ALECK BELL, *Widdemer*
CYRUS McCORMICK, *Dobler*
ELI WHITNEY, *Snow*
ELIAS HOWE, *Corcoran*
ELIZABETH BLACKWELL, *Henry*
GEORGE CARVER, *Stevenson*
GEORGE EASTMAN, *Henry*
HENRY FORD, *Aird and Ruddiman*
JOHN AUDUBON, *Mason*
LUTHER BURBANK, *Burt*
MARIA MITCHELL, *Melin*
ROBERT FULTON, *Henry*
SAMUEL MORSE, *Snow*
TOM EDISON, *Guthridge*
WALTER REED, *Higgins*
WILBUR AND ORVILLE WRIGHT, *Stevenson*
WILL AND CHARLIE MAYO, *Hammontree*

SOCIAL and

BETSY ROSS, *Weil*
BOOKER T. WASHINGTON, *Stevenson*
CLARA BARTON, *Stevenson*
DAN BEARD, *Mason*
FRANCES WILLARD, *Mason*
JANE ADDAMS, *Wagoner*
J. STERLING MORTON, *Moore*
JULIA WARD HOWE, *Wagoner*
JULIETTE LOW, *Higgins*
LILIUOKALANI, *Newman*
LUCRETIA MOTT, *Burnett*
MOLLY PITCHER, *Stevenson*
OLIVER WENDELL HOLMES, JR., *Dunham*
SUSAN ANTHONY, *Monsell*

SOLDIERS

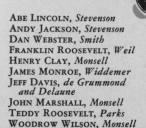

ANTHONY WAYNE, *Stevenson*
BEDFORD FORREST, *Parks*
DAN MORGAN, *Bryant*
ETHAN ALLEN, *Winders*
FRANCIS MARION, *Steele*
ISRAEL PUTNAM, *Stevenson*
JEB STUART, *Winders*
NATHANAEL GREENE, *Peckham*
ROBERT E. LEE, *Monsell*
SAM HOUSTON, *Stevenson*
TOM JACKSON, *Monsell*
U. S. GRANT, *Stevenson*
WILLIAM HENRY HARRISON, *Peckham*
ZACK TAYLOR, *Wilkie*

STATESMEN

ABE LINCOLN, *Stevenson*
ANDY JACKSON, *Stevenson*
DAN WEBSTER, *Smith*
FRANKLIN ROOSEVELT, *Weil*
HENRY CLAY, *Monsell*
JAMES MONROE, *Widdemer*
JEFF DAVIS, *de Grummond and Delaune*
JOHN MARSHALL, *Monsell*
TEDDY ROOSEVELT, *Parks*
WOODROW WILSON, *Monsell*

Walter Chrysler

Boy Machinist

Illustrated by Al Fiorentino

Walter Chrysler

Boy Machinist

By Ethel H. Weddle

THE **BOBBS-MERRILL** COMPANY, INC.
A SUBSIDIARY OF **HOWARD W. SAMS & CO., INC.**
Publishers • INDIANAPOLIS • NEW YORK

LIBRARY OF CONGRESS CATALOG CARD NUMBER: 60-8883

To my grandchildren

The author acknowledges special indebt-edness to Walter P. Chrysler, Jr., for his helpful comments and criticisms; also to the Chrysler Corporation and the Union Pacific Railroad for source materials used in the preparation of illustrations.

Illustrations

Numerous smaller illustrations

Contents

Walter Chrysler

Boy Machinist

Walter's Big Day

THE CLOCK in the kitchen was striking. Walter Chrysler sat up in bed to count the strokes of the gong. There were six.

"It's six o'clock!" he cried. "Get up, everybody! It's time to get up!"

Walter's older brother, Ed, grabbed for the blankets. "Hey, don't pull the covers off," he said. "I'm not ready to get up."

Walter jumped out of bed.

"You'd better be ready," he said. "First thing you know, you'll miss breakfast."

Ed snuggled down under the covers. "Don't be silly," he said. "I don't smell coffee or steak.

11

Besides, that train won't pull out ahead of time today just because you're going to ride on the engine. You'd better get some more sleep."

Walter paid no attention. He couldn't have slept any more if he had tried. In fact, he was so excited that he could hardly get dressed. He was sure that he was the happiest boy in Ellis, Kansas, that morning in 1883.

Ever since he could remember, he had wanted to ride on the engine with his father, who was a railroad engineer. Now at last his wish was coming true.

By the time he had finished dressing, Walter heard his mother setting the skillets on the stove. He rushed into the kitchen.

"Hurry, Mother," he said. "We'd better not be late today."

Mrs. Chrysler smiled. "Breakfast is never late in this house," she said. "Not with your father an engineer on the Union Pacific."

Walter reached for his cap and jacket. "I'll fill the woodbox before we eat."

"That's a good idea," Mrs. Chrysler agreed.

Walter ran to the woodshed. He piled his arms high with wood. Then he saw his father starting toward the barn.

"Hurry, Dad," he called. "We'd better not be late this morning." He was almost staggering under his load of wood.

"We won't," Mr. Chrysler promised.

Walter carried several armloads of wood to the kitchen. At last the big box near the stove was filled to the top.

"There!" he said to his mother. "The box is full. Is breakfast ready?"

Mrs. Chrysler was busy stirring gravy. "Yes, almost," she said. "And thank you for bringing in the wood, Walter."

By this time Ed had dressed and gone out to help Mr. Chrysler do the milking. When they came into the kitchen for breakfast, Ed began to tease Walter.

"I guess we have two engineers this morning," he said.

"You can go ahead and laugh, Ed Chrysler," Walter said quickly. "But I *am* going to be a railroadman, so there!" He stood in front of the little mirror on the wall and combed his hair. "Yes, sir," he went on, "when I grow up I'm going to work for the railroad."

"Shucks, you're too little to know what you want," Ed said. "You're only eight. Now I'm twelve and I think I'm old enough to know——"

"I'm five," said a sleepy little voice behind them. "Will I be a railroadman, too?"

The boys laughed and turned to look at their only sister, Irene. The sound of their voices had awakened her.

"You're only a girl, Irene," Ed said. "You can't do the important things that boys can."

14

"She can do things that are just as important, though," Walter said as he took his chair at the table. "She can learn to cook and fill our dinner buckets with good things to eat. When she's grown up she can wear pretty clothes and ride on the train. I'll be the engineer and I'll take her everywhere."

"Well, engineer, here's your breakfast," Mrs. Chrysler said. She placed several dishes of steaming hot food on the table and looked at the clock. "Get busy and eat if you want to be on time," she added.

The family took their places at the table. Mr. Chrysler cut and served the buffalo steak.

"M-m-m!" Walter said. "This will taste good. I'm hungry." He helped himself to fried potatoes and gravy. He put butter and molasses on a stack of pancakes. Mrs. Chrysler poured a cup of milk and set it beside his plate.

Walter always ate a good breakfast. But this

morning he ate two bites of the buffalo steak and laid down his fork.

"I can't eat," he said in a queer, tight voice. "I can't eat at all."

"What's the matter? Are you sick, Walter?" asked Mrs. Chrysler. "If you don't feel well you'd better not go with Dad today."

"I'm not sick," Walter said. "The food just sticks in my throat."

"Walter's too excited to eat," Ed said with a

laugh. "I think he's really too little to ride on Dad's engine."

"No, I'm not too little to ride," said Walter. "Besides Dad said I could go."

"Certainly you can go," said Mr. Chrysler, busily eating his usual big breakfast. "You've just got engine fever, Walter. It won't hurt you. I've been too excited to eat more than once in my life."

"May I leave the table?" asked Walter.

"Yes, but don't go away," said Mr. Chrysler. "We'll be off as soon as your mother packs our dinner buckets."

Walter put his cap on his head and slipped on his jacket. Soon his father rose from the table and took his jacket and cap from the hook on the wall. Then Walter saw that the dinner buckets were packed.

"Good-by, Mother," he said as he picked up the buckets. "I'll see you tonight."

"Good-by, son," she answered. "Have a good time. I hope you'll feel all right."

OFF FOR BROOKVILLE

Walter followed his father over a hard-beaten path. The path cut across empty lots to the railroad yards on the edge of town. The yards were not too far from the Chrysler home.

Walter walked fast to keep up with his father's long steps. As he trotted along, he looked up at his father's face.

"Look, Dad," he said. "I'm almost grown-up. I'm taller than your gun holster now."

Mr. Chrysler smiled down at him. "You're growing fast, Walter," he said. "One of these days you'll be ready for a job on the railroad."

"Then I'll wear a gun just like yours," said Walter. "And I'll be able to shoot it, too."

"It's a good idea to know how to shoot a gun,"

18

said Mr. Chrysler. "You never know what you'll meet out here on the plains."

"That's about right, sir," said Walter knowingly. "There are always wild animals and rattlesnakes around. Sometimes the Indians go on the warpath, too."

"Yes, that's about right," his father replied with a smile. "But the railroads are changing things. The wild animals are disappearing, and I doubt whether the Indians will give us much more trouble."

Before Walter and his father were halfway to the big stone station, Walter heard someone running behind him.

A familiar voice called, "Hey, Walter! Wait a minute. Where are you going?"

Walter looked back. Two of his friends, Charlie Keagy and Joe McMahon, were running to catch up with him.

"I'm going to Brookville on the engine with

my father," Walter said proudly. "I'm going to learn how the engine works."

"You don't say!" said Joe, who was a little older than Walter. "I guess you think that's something pretty big, don't you?"

"I know it is," Walter said. "We had to get special permission from the railroad."

"Humph!" said Charlie. "If I were going to get a special permit to take a ride, I'd ride in a coach. It would be a lot more fun."

"Not for me, it wouldn't," Walter said. "I'll have to hurry now, but I'll see you tomorrow. I'll tell you about the ride then."

Walter hurried to catch up with his father. When they reached the station, the train was waiting on the track. They walked along beside the coaches. They saw some passengers climbing into the coaches.

Looking through the windows, Walter saw other passengers sitting on red plush seats inside. Some were eating breakfast from baskets which they held on their laps.

These people were all traveling somewhere. Some were probably going only to the next town, but others were going far away.

"Just think," Walter said. "None of these people could go anywhere without the engineer."

"No," Mr. Chrysler agreed. "At least they couldn't go very far or very fast. The railroads are helping our country to grow. They're helping it to become a great nation."

"Then the railroads are important," Walter said. "I guess if I work for the railroad when I grow up, I'll have the most important job in the world." He felt happy and satisfied as he walked up to the engine with his father.

The engineer who had just brought the train in climbed down from the engine cab.

"Howdy," Walter said.

"Howdy, Walter," said the engineer with a

smile. He took off his gloves and wiped the back of one hand across his forehead. "Are you taking your first ride today?"

Walter nodded. Standing there beside the engine, he was suddenly too happy to speak.

"Well, I'll bet you're the most excited boy in Kansas this morning," the engineer said. He took Walter by the shoulders and gave him a friendly little shake.

Walter grinned. "I can hardly wait to get started," he said.

"I don't blame you," the engineer said. "You know, Walter, an engine is almost like something alive. It can snort and puff, and it can roll down its track pulling a great load behind it. Well, I'd better go. Have a good time, son." The engineer went on his way.

Walter laid his hand on the waiting engine. It was purring like his big old cat at home. Lazy swirls of smoke came from the smokestack.

"Charlie and Joe can tease me all they wish," Walter thought. "I don't care. I *like* engines."

Suddenly Mr. Chrysler turned to him. "Climb up, son," he said. "It's time to go."

Walter swung himself into the cab. The fireman was already in his place.

"Howdy," said the fireman. "So you're going along today."

"Yes, sir!" Walter said.

Then Mr. Chrysler came up into the cab, carrying the dinner buckets in his hand. He put them in a safe place.

"What shall I do, Dad?" Walter asked.

Mr. Chrysler pointed to a padded seat on the right side of the cab. "Sit there," he said. "And don't move unless I tell you to."

"All right, Dad, I won't," Walter promised. He crawled up on the seat. His feet did not touch the floor. The seat had been made for a tall man like his father.

"Dad," Walter said, "will I find out how the engine works today?"

"Just watch me, son," Mr. Chrysler said, "and you'll learn a lot about how it works."

"Will I learn how it's made?"

"Not today, I'm afraid, Walter. A steam engine is a very big machine. It takes more than one ride to learn how it is made."

Mr. Chrysler put his left hand on the throttle, with which he set the engine's speed. In his right hand he held his pocket watch. He leaned out the window to watch for the conductor's signal.

Walter grinned delightedly. He heard a great hissing of steam. He heard a rattle and clatter as the brakes were released. He heard the conductor shout, "All aboard!"

Mr. Chrysler put his watch in his pocket. He pulled the throttle back and the engine jerked forward. Then, with a loud snort, the engine began to move. Since his father always left on

time, Walter knew that it was exactly 7:30. He looked across at the fireman.

"We're off!" he shouted.

"Yes, we're off," the fireman answered.

As the engine gathered speed, Mr. Chrysler kept his eyes on the track ahead. Walter knew that they were headed east toward Fort Hayes. Far beyond the fort lay Brookville, the end of his father's run.

Walter watched the hand on the dial of the steam gauge. When it dropped, he saw his father nod to the fireman.

The fireman opened the door of the firebox. He stood on the platform between the engine and the coal tender and shoveled coal into the fire. He spread the coal over the firebed properly. Then he shut the door with a clang.

"Dad, must I be a good fireman before I can be an engineer?" Walter shouted.

"Yes, indeed," said Mr. Chrysler. "When you

learn to fire the engine, you can go from the left side of the cab to the right. The engineer always sits on the right side of the cab."

"I'm watching how you work the throttle," Walter said. "I want to know exactly how you do it."

"Good for you!" said Mr. Chrysler. "That's the best way to learn."

Mr. Chrysler leaned out the window so that he could see the track ahead. Walter wished that he could do that, too. But his father had told him not to move, so Walter stayed where he was. If he did as he was told, he might get to ride again. And to ride again on his father's engine was just what he wanted.

THE MORNING RIDE

They soon left Ellis far behind. By and by Walter glanced out the window. Close by, a cowboy was galloping beside the railroad tracks on his horse. Walter was surprised to see that he was going as fast as the train.

"Dad, I didn't know a horse could run as fast as an engine," he said.

"It can, but not for long," his father told him. "Soon that cowboy's horse will grow tired, but our iron horse here never grows tired." He looked at one of the dials in front of him. "We are going twenty miles an hour," he added. "Now just watch."

He opened the throttle wider. The engine began to pick up speed. Slowly but steadily the train drew ahead of the horse and rider.

The rider waved his hat. Walter saw his mouth move. Probably he was yelling, "Yip-pee! Yip-pee! Yip-pee!"

Walter waved back. "Yip-pee! We won!" he shouted happily.

Mr. Chrysler waved at the rider, too. "I've

run many races with cowboys," he said. "I've raced with buffaloes and Indians, too."

"Tell me about them," Walter begged.

"No time now," said Mr. Chrysler. "We're coming to Fort Hayes. If you keep your eyes open you'll see the soldiers."

Fort Hayes was thirteen miles from Ellis. As the train passed by, Walter saw many soldiers in their blue uniforms. Before long he turned back to the engine.

"I think the engine is more exciting than soldiers," he said.

Soon Fort Hayes was behind them, and the train was clattering over the plains again.

"Now tell me about the railroad," said Walter.

"Well, it was the first railroad to be built across the Great Plains," said Mr. Chrysler. "It tied America together."

"Tied it together?"

"Yes, it joined the East and the West closely

for the first time. It gave people a faster and easier way of crossing the country than they had had before."

"Were you working for the railroad when it was being built?" asked Walter.

"Yes, but I didn't help to lay the tracks," Mr. Chrysler explained. "I was an engineer, but the early engines weren't like the one I have now. They burned wood instead of coal."

Presently Mr. Chrysler pointed to a spot beside the tracks. "We had a fight with Indians there one day," he said. "It was too bad they couldn't understand how important the railroad was to this part of the country."

"Why didn't they want the railroad?" Walter wanted to know.

"They were afraid it would chase the buffaloes away," his father replied.

"Did it?"

"I don't know. Maybe." Mr. Chrysler looked

30

out over the plains thoughtfully, then went on. "I do know there aren't so many as there used to be. Sometimes the herds were so large that we had to stop the train. Hours would pass before the tracks would be clear."

"You should have chased them away with your whistle," Walter said.

Mr. Chrysler laughed and shook his head. "We tried that, but it didn't always work," he said. "Sometimes the herd would gallop away, and sometimes it wouldn't even move."

Walter would have liked to hear more, but it was hard to speak above the noise of the engine. Besides, the engine swayed so much that he was busy trying to stay on his bouncing seat.

If his tongue was idle, however, his eyes were not. While his father was busy running the train, Walter studied every part of the cab.

At last Mr. Chrysler looked at his watch. "It's twelve o'clock," he said. "Are you hungry?"

31

"I could eat a buffalo," Walter replied.

Mr. Chrysler laughed. He handed Walter one of the dinner buckets. "Here's your buffalo," he said. "You probably are hungry, since you didn't eat much breakfast."

Walter grinned. He opened his bucket and ate everything that his mother had packed. It all tasted wonderful.

By the time the train reached Brookville, Walter was sure he knew how his father ran his locomotive. But he had not learned much about how it was made.

At last Mr. Chrysler pulled the train up to the station. "Well, here we are," he said, "right on time. This is the end of our run."

Walter rose and stretched. "Whew! I feel as if I'm bolted to the seat. I'm glad we're here. Now I can get some exercise."

It felt good to stretch his legs. Soon he and his father were seeing the sights of Brookville.

"I'm tired of Brookville," Walter said a few hours later. "The stores are just like the stores at home, and the people are just like the people at home. I wish the train would come."

Mr. Chrysler laughed and tousled Walter's hair. "You like that engine, don't you?" he said. "Well, it won't be long. In a few more minutes the train will be in and we'll be on our way."

"Do you know what I'd like to do, Dad?" Walter asked.

"I couldn't guess," said Mr. Chrysler.

"I'd like to make an engine just like yours. A little one that would run."

"A model?" said Mr. Chrysler. "That's a fine idea, Walter. Go ahead and try. You might even make a big engine some day. Who knows?"

Night came as the train roared westward. The rest of the trip was made in darkness.

Walter did not try to talk. The engine seemed

33

to go faster at night than it had during the day. Mr. Chrysler kept his eyes on the tunnel of yellow light which the headlamp threw on the track ahead of them.

Walter clung to his seat with both hands. He squinted his eyes to protect them from cinders. He was almost as dirty as the fireman now, but he didn't care. He was thinking about what he would tell Joe and Charlie tomorrow.

He would rather ride in a coach, Charlie had said! But he didn't know how exciting it was to ride in the engine with the engineer. He didn't know about the shrill scream of the whistle or the glowing red light of the fire. He had never looked out the window and seen the long yellow tunnel of light made by the headlamp.

Things like these helped Walter to see how exciting and important the railroad was. He knew that a person had to ride in the engine to know about them.

When he reached home that evening Walter was smiling happily. His mother started to ask questions, but he was too tired to answer.

Mrs. Chrysler smiled. "You've had a big day, haven't you, son?" she said. "I never saw such a happy boy."

"I never saw a boy who understands things so quickly," Mr. Chrysler said. "When I explain something to Walter, he listens. I don't have to tell him twice."

"That's good," Mrs. Chrysler said. "Maybe he'll do something big someday."

Walter tumbled into bed beside Ed. Even after he had fallen asleep, he was still smiling.

Ordinary Days

It HAD been two years since Walter's first ride on his father's locomotive. One morning he and Ed ran to the barn to do the morning chores. Each of them carried a milk bucket.

Walter stopped beside the cow that he was going to milk. He patted her neck and stroked her back. "So-o-o, Daisy! So-o!" he said.

He sat down on his milking stool and held the bucket with his knees. His strong hands made the milk squirt into the tin bucket with a musical sound. But he paid little attention. He was listening to Ed, who was talking to himself in the next stall.

"What are you saying, Ed?" Walter asked. "I can't understand you."

"I don't like to milk cows twice a day," Ed said. "I'm glad that I'm older than you are. I'll be old enough to work in the railroad shops soon. When I go to work in the shops, you'll have to do the milking."

"Well, I don't like to milk cows any better than you do," Walter said. "I'd much rather work on the little engine I'm trying to make. I really think Dad should make you milk the cows, because you're older than I am."

"Oh, come along," Ed said. "That argument won't work. It was Dad who said it's about time for me to work at the shops and time for you to milk these cows."

Walter knew that nothing would change his father's plans. But he said, "I don't see why we have to run a farm right here in Ellis. Every time I start to work on my engine somebody says, 'Walter, milk the cows.' Or, 'Walter, feed the pigs.' Or, 'Walter, feed the chickens.' "

"Or, 'Walter, work in the garden.' "

Walter and Ed turned in surprise. It was Mrs. Chrysler speaking. She had come to the barn to get grain for the chickens.

"Yes, and the garden," Walter laughed.

Mrs. Chrysler thought for a moment. Then she said, "Walter, what do you think we'd eat if we didn't have cows and pigs and chickens and the garden to give us food?"

"Some people don't have them, and I guess they eat," Walter said.

"Yes, but they spend their money buying beans and pork," declared Mrs. Chrysler. "Now we think that we should save our money. If we do, some day we'll have saved enough to do something special."

Mrs. Chrysler took some grain from the bin. Walter didn't say anything.

"Besides," she went on, "who wants to eat beans and pork all the time? That kind of food won't make you healthy and strong."

Walter thought of all the good food his mother prepared for the table.

"It would grow tiresome," he said.

Mrs. Chrysler turned to leave the barn. "Anyway," she said, "you must remember that work— any kind of work—is good for you. It makes you grow in more ways than one."

Walter watched the foam rise as the milk began to fill his bucket. He thought about the things his mother had said.

Finally he turned to Ed. "I'm only ten," he said. "It's going to be a long time before I'm grown up enough to work on the railroad. But I suppose Mother's right. I guess the work here at home will be good for me."

Just then the boys heard shouting voices and galloping horses and pistol shots.

"Cowboys!" Walter yelled. Setting his bucket of milk aside, he jumped up and ran to watch a group of cowboys riding into town.

"Yip-pee!" they shouted. They threw their hats into the air and fired their pistols.

"They're in town for a holiday," said Ed. "And they're certainly here bright and early."

The boys finished milking, turned the cows loose, and took the milk into the house.

"Well, I think I'd rather be a railroadman than a cowboy," Walter said. "But let's hurry. Maybe if we follow those fellows we can find some cartridges that they have lost."

"Let's do," Ed said. "Then we can pick up the cartridges and save them for Dad."

STORIES IN THE EVENING

"Company's coming," Walter announced from the door one evening.

41

"Oh, goody!" cried Irene.

"Suits me, too," said Walter. "I like to have the neighbors sitting around the kitchen. I like the stories they tell."

"It isn't the stories that I like so much," said Irene. "I like to play with the girls."

"Girls are fraidy-cats," Walter teased. "They run off to play because they don't like to hear about fights with the Indians. They don't want to hear how General Custer and his men were killed. They don't want to hear how the Indians attacked Dad's work train and how the soldiers from Fort Hayes came to the rescue."

"Girls are not fraidy-cats!" Irene declared. "What about that woman over in Rawlins County who was carried away by the Indians? I guess she wasn't a fraidy-cat. She scattered pieces of her apron along the trail so that her friends could follow her."

Before long the Chryslers' kitchen was full of

neighbors, who came to talk and tell stories until bedtime.

Irene asked the girls into the bedroom to play, but the boys sat around on the floor. They listened to exciting stories until their hair stood on end and chills ran up and down their spines.

"Come on," Joe said at last. "I'm tired of sitting. Let's go outside and play."

"Go on if you want to," Walter said, "but I'm going to stay right here. I want to hear about the Indian scare that we had here in Ellis. I can remember that."

"That scare really was a joke," said Mr. Chrysler with a smile.

"It wasn't a joke to me," said Walter. "I was going to the store that morning to get oil for the lamps. Along came Tall John running as fast as he could. 'Indians!' he yelled. 'Indians are coming! Run and hide!'"

"And, boy, how you ran!" said one of the neighbors with a grin.

Walter grinned, too, but his eyes were big and bright with excitement. "Yes, sir, I ran! I got home and tumbled into the storm cellar. But Mother dragged me out and we all went to the railroad station."

"I kept telling everyone it was a mistake," said Mrs. Chrysler. "There was the telegraph instrument clicking away in the express office all day long. No warning of any kind came from the fort. And not one of us had enough sense to use the telegraph to find out whether the Indians were coming or not."

"It was quieter than a church in that station," said Walter. "The women wouldn't let us boys say a word. They just talked in whispers."

Others added to the story.

"All the able-bodied men were gone on the work train," one said.

"And never an Indian came," another added.

"When we came home with the work train that evening, we were all puzzled," said Mr. Chrysler. "The women and children came running out of the station to meet us. We didn't know whether to be frightened or surprised."

"It turned out to be a right good surprise," said Mrs. Chrysler with a happy laugh.

She set a huge platter of cookies on the table and poured glasses of milk for the children to drink. She poured black coffee from the big old pot on the stove for the men and women. At last the visitors went home.

"I wish they'd stay and talk all night," said Walter. "I'd like to hear more."

THE TRUTH ABOUT GOING TO SCHOOL

"Hey, Walt! Are you ready for school?" Walter looked up. Charlie Keagy and Joe McMahon were calling from the corner.

"I'm coming," Walter shouted. He dashed down the street to catch up with them.

All the boys and girls in Ellis were eager to start to school this fall. A large new stone school building had been erected for the growing city. The pupils were all wondering what it would be like to attend school in such a fine building.

"There are big blackboards on some of the walls," Charlie said.

"And enough desks for everyone," said Joe.

"No one will have to sit on benches without backs any longer."

"That may be so," Walter said, "but I'll bet the teacher makes us study harder than ever."

The pupils soon found that school was just the same as before. There were reading and spelling, writing and arithmetic. Now that he was older, Walter found that geography and history had been added to his work.

Late one afternoon, Walter was sitting at his desk. He was supposed to be writing the multiplication tables on his slate. But his slate pencil hung idle between his fingers.

"I don't feel like studying today," he thought for the twentieth time. The sounds that were coming through the open windows were too interesting to let him study.

He heard an engine give four short blasts of its whistle. That was the engineer's call asking for signals.

He heard another engine give one short blast. That meant apply the brakes and stop.

He heard still another engine give three short blasts. He knew that that engine was standing still and was about to back up.

Finally he heard two long blasts. "Release the brakes and proceed," he said aloud.

Everyone looked at him. The girls giggled. The boys roared with laughter. The teacher looked stern.

Walter returned the teacher's look with a shamefaced grin. He hadn't meant to speak aloud. But now that he had, he knew that he would have to take the consequences.

"Walter Chrysler, you may stay after school tonight," the teacher said. "You've been inattentive all day. We'll do today's lessons over and over until you know them."

"But I can't stay after school," Walter said. "I must milk the cows."

"There will be time to milk the cows after you do your lessons," said the teacher.

When the teacher finally let him go, Walter ran all the way home. Mrs. Chrysler met him at the door. She handed him the milk bucket without saying a word.

When he returned to the kitchen, Walter said, "The teacher kept me after school, Mother."

"So that's it," Mrs. Chrysler said. "Why?"

Walter told her. "I've got to know the signals, Mother," he said. "You know I do if I'm going to be a railroadman."

"Walter, what you are learning at school comes first," she said. "You must pay attention to your lessons. You must learn to read and spell and write. Above all, you must learn arithmetic. You'll never be a good engineer or have a good position with the railroad if you don't know these things."

"Honest?" Walter said in surprise.

"Just as sure as we're standing here in this kitchen," said Mrs. Chrysler firmly, "you'll never get a good job if you don't know the things you learn at school."

Walter looked at his mother. She was slicing bread for supper. She looked very serious. He saw that she meant exactly what she said. His face became serious, too.

"All right, Mother," he said. "After this I'll study hard. I'll do all my lessons right and do everything the teacher tells me to do."

Walter kept his promise. It wasn't always easy. But before the winter was over, he was getting good grades.

One day Joe said, "Walt, what's happened to you? You're studying like a fool."

"Yes," Charlie said, "you act as if you really like to study."

"You know something?" Walter said. "I've discovered that I do, especially arithmetic. I'm going to learn all that I can about arithmetic. It will help me to be a railroadman when I'm old enough to work."

"Are you going home now?"

"No, I'm going over to the railroad yards," Walter said. "I see a new engine there."

Walter ran toward the tracks. He hoped that he knew the engineer in charge of the engine. Then he could ask for permission to take a good look at it.

The engineer turned out to be one of his father's good friends.

"Climb up, Walter," he said. "I can't let you stay long, but I'll show you a new part that has just been added to this engine."

"Thank you," Walter said. "Did you know I am trying to build an engine of my own?"

"A real engine?"

"Well, a little one," Walter said. "But it's going to run. At least I hope it will."

"Yow-ee!" Walter yelled. He had just jumped out of bed into several inches of snow. He had heard the wind shrieking around the house all night long. Now he knew that it must have snowed all night, too.

Just then Mr. Chrysler opened the door. "What's going on in here, boys?" he asked.

"There's a whole snowbank in here," Walter said. "And I jumped right into it." He dashed past his father and ran to dry his feet by the kitchen stove.

Ed burst from the bedroom, shaking snow from his feet, too. "The snow's blowing in around the windows," he said.

"Why don't we put up a new house, Dad?" Walter asked. He had pulled on the long woolen stockings which his mother had made for him. Now he was pulling on his boots.

"Well," said Mr. Chrysler, "that's exactly what

we're going to do. We've saved almost enough money to buy the lumber. When we've saved a little more, you boys can help me and we'll build a new home."

Walter looked at his mother, and his mother looked at him.

"See?" she said. "See what fine things we can plan to do when we save our money?"

Walter and Ed pulled on their warm clothes and started for the barn to do the chores. Walter was not thinking about the chores. He was thinking about saving money. If you saved money, you could buy something that you really wanted or needed.

He thought about the little steam engine that he was trying to build. Although he had not gone far with his work, he had already discovered that he needed special tools to cut pieces of metal and to bore holes in them.

"I think I'll try to save some money," he said.

"Then I'd have money to buy things that I want. Maybe I could even buy some tools."

Ed opened the barn door. Walter followed him inside. It was warm in the barn. When they heard the boys coming, the horses nickered and the cows lowed softly.

Ed reached for the grain measure.

"I don't know what money you're going to save, Walt," he said. "You know you won't have any money until you're old enough to work in the shops. There aren't many ways for boys to earn money in this town."

Walter hung his head. Ed was right. The boys in Ellis seldom had any money. Then his face brightened. "Well, if I can't save enough money to buy tools, maybe I could make some. I'll bet I *could* make tools if I tried."

"Why do you need tools, Walt?" Ed asked. "You can use Dad's if you want to."

Walter began to pitch hay to the cows.

"I have been using them," he said, "but he doesn't have everything I need. Besides, I'm afraid I'll ruin them. Most of Dad's tools are for working in wood, and I'm making my engine out of metal."

Ed stopped working and looked at Walter.

"Do you mean that you've really started to make that engine?"

"Yes."

"Is it going to run?"

"I hope so," Walter said, "but I don't know. I'm afraid it isn't very well made."

"Who ever heard of a boy your age making a locomotive?" Ed asked with a little laugh.

"Maybe no one," Walter said. "But when I've made mine, you will have heard of it."

One Eye on
the Railroad

By THE SPRING of 1887, Ellis was a busy, hustling place. It was growing even faster than the Chrysler children. Walter was twelve now, and Irene was nine. Ed had finished school and was working in the railroad shops. Usually Walter did all the chores by himself.

One spring morning Irene offered to help him. "I'll feed the chickens for you," she said.

"Thank you," said Walter. "I've pumped the water to fill the water tank, and I've cleaned the barn. If you feed the chickens, I'll ask Mother what she wants me to do next."

"It's a fine morning, but I think it's going to

turn warm," Mrs. Chrysler said. "Pump enough water to fill the tub in the storm cellar. I'll put the milk in the tub to keep it cool and sweet. Then we'll plant some corn and beans and pumpkins while Irene bakes some cookies."

Walter trudged back and forth from the well to the storm cellar. By and by the big tub was filled with cold water.

"It's a good thing I like cold milk to drink," he said. "If I didn't, I'm afraid I wouldn't like the job of filling this tub."

At that moment Mrs. Chrysler came from the house with a basket of seeds.

"Thanks to plenty of milk, you're tall and strong for your age," she said. "Don't forget that. Bring both hoes to the garden."

"I'm learning to appreciate this work in the garden," Walter said. "I can hear the train whistles while I'm helping you. I can even see the trains down on the tracks."

Mrs. Chrysler smiled. "I can see you aren't happy unless you have one eye on the railroad."

"Both eyes would be even better," Walter answered with a laugh.

"Well, I'll try to give you as much time as possible," Mrs. Chrysler said. "Just now I think you'd better keep both eyes on the garden. I can't stand weeds. And I don't want you to chop down the corn by accident, either."

In the middle of the morning Irene came from the house. "I've brought you some cold water and some molasses cookies," she said. "I just made the cookies."

Walter took a big bite out of a cookie. "Mm-m! It's good!" he said. "You'll be a good cook like Mother, Irene. And one thing sure, when I'm a railroad engineer I'll take you for a ride on my train."

Irene laughed. "You've been promising me that for a long time."

59

"I won't forget it," Walter said.

After lunch Mrs. Chrysler said, "Walter, it's too hot to work in the garden this afternoon. Why don't you run on and play with your friends until evening? Be sure to get back in time to do your evening chores."

"Whoopee!" shouted Walter. "Don't worry, Mother, I'll be back in time."

He ran off toward the railroad yards.

As he ran, he wondered whether he would find any of his engineer friends at the yards. He hoped he would, because he wanted to get up in the cab. He wanted to study the levers and valves which the engineer used to run the engine. He wanted to sit in the engineer's seat and play that he was an engineer himself.

When he reached the yards, he looked around quickly. Two engines were moving slowly along on different tracks, and a third was standing motionless on a near-by siding. A little smoke came from its smokestack, but no one was in it or near it.

Walter looked at the engine longingly. "This would be a good time to look at those valves," he thought. "There's nobody around to bother me." He moved forward a step or two, then suddenly stopped.

"Dad told me never to get on an engine without the engineer's permission," he thought. "I'd better wait. Maybe he'll come along."

He walked toward the station with his hands deep in his pockets. The sun was hot on his bare head. The black cinders were hot and sharp under his bare feet.

Suddenly one hand found the marbles that he always carried in his pocket. "We ought to have a game," he thought. He looked around. Down the street he saw a group of his friends.

"Hey, fellows!" he yelled. "Come on over and play marbles!"

Several of the boys came running toward him. Among them were Charlie Keagy and Joe McMahon.

"Let's go," Charlie Keagy said. "Walt, you draw the circle. Nobody can make as good a circle as you can."

"All right," Walter said. He picked up a stick and made a mark in the cinders. "Each of you start here," he went on. "Take ten short steps in different directions. Then I'll draw a big circle where you stop."

When the boys had stopped, Walter made a curving line from one boy to the next. When he had finished, he had drawn a big circle.

"That's fine," said Charlie with admiration. "It takes Walter to measure things right."

The boys reached into their pockets and took out their marbles.

"I have five keesters, two agates, and three glassies," Joe McMahon said.

62

"You're lucky," Charlie said. "I just have six, counting my taw."

"You're lucky, too," said a third boy. "All I have is three keesters. I'll have to keep sharp watch until I find a taw."

Walter nodded. There wasn't a boy in Ellis who had the money to buy marbles.

"We're lucky the men like to play," Charlie said. "We wouldn't have any marbles at all if we didn't pick up the ones they lose."

Walter grinned. "I guess I followed a man with a hole in his pocket," he said. He brought out a big handful of marbles.

The other boys opened their eyes wide.

"Talk about luck!" Joe said.

"It isn't luck," said Charlie. "Don't forget, that boy's the marble champion of Ellis."

Walter looked thoughtful. "You know, I think the best luck we could have would be to find some way to earn a little money. If we had money we could buy our own marbles or anything else we needed."

The boys hooted.

"How could we earn money here?" asked one.

"You've got to be old enough to work in the machine shops," said another.

"There's not an odd job in the whole town," said a third.

"Well, come on," Joe said. "Let's play."

"Who goes first?"

Walter sat back on his heels to wait his turn. But he was not thinking about the game. He was wondering how he could earn some money.

Before his turn came to knuckle down on the edge of the ring, he heard a faint, far-off whistle.

"Train's coming!" he shouted. He dashed off toward the tracks.

"Hey!" called the boys. "It's your turn."

Walter waved his hand. "Go ahead," he called. "I'd rather watch the train come in."

"Wait a minute," Joe yelled. "There are plenty here without me, too. I'm going with you."

The two boys disappeared around the corner of the station.

NEW THINGS COME TO ELLIS

The freight agent and his helpers were rolling big hand trucks toward the tracks. The iron wheels crunched over the hard-packed cinders.

Walter and Joe stood by the tracks with their feet planted wide apart. They heard the engineer blow the signal to stop.

"It's the westbound freight," said Walter. "It sounds as if the engine's pulling a heavy load."

The boys stepped away from the track. Soon the engine came puffing past them. Walter shouted "Howdy" to the engineer, who was one of his father's friends. He ran beside the engine until it came to a stop.

"How's Number Eight doing today?" he shouted as the engineer climbed down from the cab of the engine.

"She's running smooth as velvet," said the engineer. "There's not a knock in her."

Walter looked at the engine for a moment. Then he walked around it twice, admiring the big drive wheels. He listened happily to the hiss of steam escaping from the boiler.

"Smooth as velvet," he thought. "That's the way a good engineer keeps his engine."

He walked back to the engineer, who held a long-nosed oilcan in one hand.

"Do you have a big load today?" he asked.

"I'll say we have," answered the engineer. He began to squirt oil into the oil cups along the drive shafts. "It's the longest and heaviest train I've ever pulled. Many people are moving west these days."

"Yes, sir," Walter said, "I guess they are. They

couldn't move without the railroad, though, could they?"

"No, they couldn't," said the engineer. "A few people used to travel in covered wagons. But now that the railroads have made traveling easy, people are moving by the thousands."

"Hey! Look!" Joe shouted suddenly. "A lot of your freight is going to be unloaded here."

"That's right, son," said the engineer. "The conductor told me there's a lot of freight for Ellis today."

The boys walked along the train. They were careful to stay out of the way, but they also tried to see all that was happening.

Boxes and barrels were being unloaded from some of the freight cars.

"I wonder what's in them," Walter said. "I'll bet there are sugar and flour and salt in those barrels. Beans, too, maybe."

"Yes, and I'll bet those boxes are full of shoes

68

and boots and dishes and things like that," Joe said. "Don't you?"

The boys went on to the next car. Here cookstoves, beds, tables, and chairs were being unloaded onto the hand trucks.

"Who's going to buy all this stuff?" Walter asked the freight agent, who happened along at that moment.

"Why, all the new people who are moving to Ellis," the agent replied. "Two dozen new families have come here in the last two weeks. I tell you, everybody's moving to Kansas."

Taking off his cap, he wiped the sweat from his face with a big red handkerchief.

"I guess you're right," said Walter.

"I am right," said the agent. "They say people will be coming all summer. There's no end to the people who want to live in the West." He turned to the loaded truck.

"Want us to help push it?" Walter asked.

"I wouldn't mind," the agent said.

Walter and Joe put their shoulders to the truck and helped roll it to the warehouse.

There it would be unloaded after the train was gone. Then the boys hurried back to the tracks. This was one of the busiest days either of them had ever seen.

Now the engineer and his crew were backing several loaded freight cars on a siding and picking up several empties. Presently the engineer blew the whistle twice.

"The train's leaving!" Walter shouted. He ran toward the engine, waving his hand. He reached it just as it moved off with a snort and a roar of steam. "Good-by!" he cried. "Good-by!"

The engineer waved a gloved hand. "Good-by, Walter," he shouted. "See you next trip."

Walter stopped and watched the cars clatter past, slowly picking up speed.

Joe tugged at his sleeve. "Look, Walter," he

said. "Look at that box." He pointed at several men struggling to take a huge box out of a boxcar. "I wonder what could be in it?"

The freight agent rushed forward. "Careful, men!" he shouted. "Be careful of that box! That's Miss Cartwright's piano."

"A piano!" Joe exclaimed. "Imagine that!"

"Well, I guess that's the first piano to come to Ellis," Walter said.

Even after the train had gone, the boys lingered to watch the freight handlers unload the cars. To Walter this was almost as exciting and thrilling as seeing the trains themselves.

"You know, Joe," he said at last, "the railroad's about the most exciting thing I know. And the most important."

"I guess maybe you're right," Joe said. "Anyway, people would have an awful time getting to Kansas without a railroad."

"Or to California," Walter said.

"Or to Texas," added Joe.

Walter put his hands in his pockets. He stood straight and tall.

"Yes, sir," he said. "The most important job I can think of is to be a good railroadman."

Suddenly he struck his head with the palm of his hand. "Oh, oh! I'm wrong! The most important thing I can think of right now is to get home and milk those cows!"

Walter and the Cows

WALTER CHOPPED the soil vigorously with his hoe. He was going to finish hoeing the corn before noon if it killed him.

Mrs. Chrysler was hoeing beans. "Be careful, Walter," she called. "Don't cut those pumpkin vines growing between the corn rows."

Walter grinned. "Don't worry," he said. "I'll be careful. I know how good pumpkin pies will taste next winter. But——"

"But what?" asked Irene. She had just brought some cookies and cold water.

"I wish I could do something to earn some money," Walter went on.

"What would you do with money if you had it?" asked Irene curiously.

"That's what I'd like to know," said Mrs. Chrysler. "You have everything a boy needs. Food, clothes, schoolbooks, and a good home. Now that Ed is working, we'll soon have enough money to build the new house."

"Yes, that's true," Walter said. "But I still would like to earn my own money. Then if I wanted anything I'd have the money to buy it. I wouldn't have to ask you or Dad."

"If you had money, are you sure you wouldn't throw it away on candy or marbles or something else?" asked Mrs. Chrysler.

"I know I wouldn't," Walter said. "There are many things I'd rather have than candy."

Mrs. Chrysler shook her head. "I don't know how you can earn money until you're older. But if you want to see what you can do, why don't you try selling milk?"

74

"Milk!" gasped Walter in astonishment.

"Yes," she replied. "Many people who have moved to Ellis lately don't keep cows. Almost every day someone comes to the door, asking to buy milk from us."

"Oh, Mother," said Walter. "I'd much rather sell something else."

"I know," said Mrs. Chrysler, "but over a period of time, I believe you could make more money by selling milk."

"We have only two cows," Walter objected, "and we use most of the milk ourselves."

"Your father and I have talked the matter over," Mrs. Chrysler went on. "We will buy another cow. Then, if you will do the milking and sell the milk, we will pay you a commission on every quart that you sell."

"Milk three cows!" exclaimed Walter. "Oh, Mother, I hate to milk cows!"

"Just think about it a moment," said Mrs.

Chrysler patiently. "People always need milk. You won't need to worry about selling it."

Walter sighed. "That makes sense all right," he said. "I'll admit that. But it certainly doesn't sound very interesting."

He looked down at the corn once more, thinking. It *would* be nice to earn money regularly, week after week. In fact, the more he thought about it, the better he liked the idea. At last he looked up with a smile.

"All right, Mother," he said, "I'll do it. I still don't like to milk cows, but I can recognize a good business when I see it."

"That makes me very happy, Walter," Mrs. Chrysler said with a proud smile. "I'm sure it's a good way for you to earn your own money."

"Please remember one thing, though," Walter added. "When I finish high school, I want to work in the railroad shops. What I really want to be is a machinist for the Union Pacific."

76

"I'll remember, Walter," his mother said.

She went to the kitchen cupboard. "Now how would you like a piece of fresh plum pie?" she asked with a smile.

WALTER, THE MILKMAN

Each evening after that Walter went up and down the streets of Ellis selling milk. Housewives came to their doors with milk jars. "How much do you charge?" they asked.

"Five cents a quart," Walter said.

When all the milk was delivered, he went over his route again, selling cream. He found that selling milk and cream took most of his time.

"Well, Walter, how's the milk business?" Ed asked one evening about a week later.

"It'll do," Walter said.

"How much do you make?"

"Mother gives me a penny for each quart of

milk I sell and a penny for each cup of cream. I've made a dollar in six days."

"Not bad," Ed said. "Not bad at all. I suppose you make more on some days than you do on others."

"Yes," said Walter. "I'm making a record sheet for orders and deliveries. I thought that would make the work easier."

"I'm glad to see you can figure out the best way to carry on a business," Ed said.

Walter delivered milk all through the long summer evenings.

One evening he met Joe McMahon and Charlie Keagy on the street.

"Will you get done with your work in time to play ball tonight?" Joe asked.

"I doubt it," Walter said.

"We miss you," said Charlie. "You used to play with the gang all the time. Now we hardly ever see you."

"I guess that's right," Walter said, a little sadly. "I guess things change when a fellow begins to grow up. He doesn't have much time left to play with his friends."

Walter went on with his deliveries. His bare feet plopped in the thick dust of the street. By the time he finished he was hot and tired.

His father was home that evening. He looked at Walter and smiled.

Walter tried to grin good-naturedly. "This is a tiresome job," he said.

"It probably is," said Mr. Chrysler. "But Mother tells me you're doing fine with it. I must say, you look about as tired and dirty as I do when I come off the engine."

Tired as he was, Walter drew himself up proudly. "That's exactly how I want to look, Dad," he said. "I want to get used to heat and dust and cold and snow. Then I'll be good and tough when I start out as a railroadman."

Mr. Chrysler put his hands on Walter's shoulders. "I'm proud of you, son. I like the way you're learning to think for yourself. I like the way you accept what seems best. You're only a boy on the Kansas prairie now. But you have as good a chance to become a great man as anyone else in America. Don't forget that."

Walter grinned. "Maybe I'll never be great, but I'll promise you one thing, Dad. I'll never forget to go on thinking for myself."

Walter Goes into Business

AFTER DINNER one summer day Walter hunted up Charlie Keagy.

"Let's go over to the railroad yards," he said.

"What for? It isn't time for a train to come in," Charlie said.

"No, but there's always something to see there," Walter replied.

Everything was quiet at the yards, however. No engines were coming or going.

"Let's go inside the station," Walter said. "It'll be cool in there."

Inside the stone walls of the station there was only the click-click-click of the telegraph

81

instruments. The boys dropped down on a bench to rest for a while.

Someone had left some magazines lying on the bench. Walter picked one up and leafed through it. As he turned the page, a small advertisement caught his eye.

> SELL our beautiful calling cards. Printed in glossy colors. Artistic designs. Send for samples. One dozen free with your name for introducing our line.

"Hey, listen to this!" he said

He read the advertisement to Charlie.

"You couldn't sell calling cards in Ellis," Charlie said.

Walter read the advertisement again. "I'd like to know why not," he said.

The more he thought about it, the more certain Walter was that he could sell the cards.

First of all, though, he'd have to get his mother's permission. He hurried home with the magazine to show her the advertisement.

"Humph!" said Mrs. Chrysler. "I'm afraid the ladies of Ellis aren't stylish enough to use calling cards, Walter."

"Oh, yes, they are," said Walter eagerly. "And if they aren't now, they will be when they get the cards. Please let me send for the samples, Mother. I know I can sell cards here."

"Well," Mrs. Chrysler said, "I guess there won't be any harm in sending for the samples."

"Thanks, Mother," Walter said. "I'll have your name printed on the free cards."

CALLING CARDS FOR ELLIS

Walter could hardly wait until the sample cards came. He let a few days go by. Then he began to haunt the post office. Day after day he was disappointed. Day after day his hopes sank lower. Perhaps his letter had been lost.

One morning when Walter reached the post office, the postmaster was reading the address on a large brown envelope.

"Walter Chrysler," he read. He peered over the top of his spectacles. "Is that you?"

Walter was so excited he couldn't answer.

"What's the matter, boy?" the postmaster said with a grin. "Has the cat got your tongue?"

Walter seized the envelope. "No, sir!" he shouted. "I mean, yes, sir, that's me!"

He ran home with the package as fast as he could. He rushed into the house.

"Mother!" he shouted. "Mother, they've come! The calling cards have come!"

Walter tore open the envelope and spread the samples out on the table. There were twelve free colored cards. There was also a catalog sheet with illustrations of other cards.

Walter examined the small white cards. They were cut with wavy edges, and a glossy cut-out picture decorated each card.

"Oh, Mother, look!" he cried. "Did you ever see anything prettier?"

Through a cluster of red roses and another of blue forget-me-nots two beautiful hands met and clasped. Walter lifted the design, which was glued to the card at one end. Under the flowers was his mother's name: MRS. HENRY CHRYSLER.

Proudly Walter held the card at arm's length. "What do you think of that, Mother?"

"Why, it's lovely!" Mrs. Chrysler cried. "I had no idea the cards would be so pretty."

"Now you'll have to dress up and visit twelve of your friends," Walter said. "You'll have to give each of them one of your cards."

"Oh, yes," Irene said. "And the ladies will say, 'Why, Mrs. Chrysler, where did you get this beautiful card?' "

"And you'll say, 'Why, from my son Walter. He's selling them, you know,' " Walter added.

They all laughed.

"I'm sure I can sell the cards even if you don't help me, Mother," Walter said.

"I can see you're going to be a good business-man," Mrs. Chrysler told him. "And that's all right. Kansas is going to need good business-men. Now run along and work hard."

Soon Walter was selling calling cards all over

Ellis. He was so busy showing samples that he had little time for anything else, even for watching trains.

One evening Mr. Chrysler was watching Walter write an order. "Well, Walter, I see you understand how to write an order," he said.

"Yes sir," Walter answered. "A businessman has to know about that. I can add all my sales and I can subtract the amount of commission I've earned. I guess my work in arithmetic is beginning to pay off."

Mr. Chrysler took Walter's neat order sheet and looked at it closely. "This is very good," he said. "I'm proud of you, Walter"

Walter beamed.

Ed looked up from the latest copy of his favorite magazine, the *Scientific American*. It was Walter's favorite, too. "Wait till you study algebra and geometry," he said. "Then you'll think arithmetic was a snap."

"I'm not scared," Walter said. "I'm not looking for a snap. I want to learn."

WALTER GOES TO THE STORE

One Saturday morning Walter went to the store. It was really a grocery store, but Mr. Henderson, the owner, sold other things as well, including hardware. It was the hardware that Walter wanted to see this morning.

As Walter opened the door, Mr. Henderson came forward to greet him.

"Good morning, Mr. Henderson," Walter said. "May I look at your tools?"

"Of course," said Mr. Henderson with a smile. "You may look as long as you wish. I think you know where they are."

"Yes, sir!" Walter hurried to the back of the store. There, behind a counter, various kinds of tools hung on the wall. There were hammers and saws, wrenches and pliers, chisels and screw drivers. There were axes and hatchets and knives, shovels and spades and hoes.

Walter leaned against the counter happily and studied the tools one by one. There was something exciting about tools, something almost adventuresome. He could have spent hours studying them to see how they were made.

Presently Mr. Henderson joined him. He put one hand on Walter's shoulder.

"Well, Walter, have you decided which ones you'd like to buy?"

"All of them!" Walter said with a grin.

"You would need a great deal of money to buy all those tools," Mr. Henderson said.

"I know," said Walter. "But why do I have to *buy* tools? Why can't I make them?"

Mr. Henderson shook his head doubtfully. "That would be a pretty big job for a boy, wouldn't it, Walter?"

"I'll bet I could do it," Walter said eagerly. "I just know I could."

WALTER SELLS SILVERWARE

That evening after supper Walter was lying on the floor reading a magazine.

Presently Irene came into the room. "What are you doing, Walter?" she asked.

"Just looking," he answered. "I'm hunting something else that I can sell. I think I've sold all the calling cards that I can."

By and by he jumped to his feet.

"I've found it!" he shouted. "Silverware! Listen. This advertisement says you can get a sample case containing three knives, three forks, and three spoons. I could take orders for sets of six. Don't you think I could sell silverware here in Ellis, Mother?"

Mrs. Chrysler quit her work and came over

to look at the magazine. She read the advertisement through carefully.

"Yes," she said, "I think the ladies in Ellis would like to buy silverware."

"Then I'll order the sample kit today," Walter said enthusiastically.

In a few days the kit arrived. Walter opened the package and found a black case with nickel clasps. He gave a delighted whistle as he opened it. "Mother! Irene! Look!" he called.

The lid was lined with white satin. The box was soft with red plush. The plush was laid in deep folds. In these folds were fitted the knives, forks, and spoons.

"Why, everyone will buy this!" cried Irene. "Oh, Walter, you'll get rich!"

"You bet I will!" Walter exclaimed. His eyes were shining with pleasure. "This——"

"Wait a minute," Mrs. Chrysler said. "You may get rich some day, but not by selling this silverware. Don't set your hopes too high, son. This silverware's pretty, but it costs much more than calling cards."

"I know that, Mother," Walter said. "But people will get more for their money, too."

Mrs. Chrysler had been looking at the case and its contents. She closed the lid and said, "That's true, Walter. But every woman in Ellis will have to ask her husband for the money."

"That means most of the men will think their old iron knives and forks are good enough," added Irene.

"I hadn't thought of that," Walter said. "I'll have to talk fast, won't I?"

He stepped up to his mother.

"Mrs. Chrysler, can't I sell you a set of this lovely silverware?"

"I don't know," said Mrs. Chrysler. "I'll have to ask my husband for the money."

Walter and his mother and Irene laughed.

92

Soon Walter began calling on the ladies of Ellis to show them his silverware. He found that his mother was right. When he opened the case, each lady would exclaim, "Oh, how beautiful!"

But soon she would say, "I'll have to talk it over with my husband. Would you please come back when he's here?"

At last, after Walter had heard this story a dozen times, he said, "I know what I'm going to do. From now on I'm going to go to the man of the house first."

Sure enough, this method worked better.

"Mister," Walter would say, "let me show you a set of silverware that will make a beautiful gift for your wife."

Many of the men growled. They said, "My wife doesn't need anything fancy. Run along."

But others said, "Well, it's been a long time since I gave my wife a present. I couldn't buy anything that would please her more."

Then they would order a set of six or twelve each of knives, forks, and spoons.

At last Walter realized that he had sold silverware to everyone who was interested.

"I think I'll stop selling it and try something else," he said one morning at breakfast. "It's been hard work, but it was worth while."

"Have you saved your commissions?" Mr. Chrysler wanted to know.

"Yes, I have," Walter said. "Every penny. I was planning to buy tools with the money, but I've decided now to save it for something else. I'm going to *make* my tools."

"Make them?"

"Yes, sir!" Walter said enthusiastically. "I know I can, Dad. I'll just copy yours out in the tool shed, and the ones I can't make here at home I can make at the blacksmith shop. I'm sure the blacksmith will let me."

A Band for Ellis

"MOTHER," WALTER called one spring morning as he smeared black polish on his shoes. "May I go to church in my clean overalls today?"

Mrs. Chrysler was busy tying Irene's hair ribbon. "Dear me, no!" she answered. "What a foolish question!"

"But I'd like church better if I didn't have to dress up," Walter said.

"Just finish polishing your shoes," Mrs. Chrysler said. "Then put on your Sunday suit, and don't waste time. Ed, I'll help you with that collar button if you'll wait a moment."

Walter sighed. His mother went to so much

trouble on Sunday morning! She always made him dress up for church.

"Cheer up, Walt," Ed said. "Just wait till you have to wear a stiff collar. Then you'll have something to growl about." He lifted his chin as Mrs. Chrysler's sure fingers fastened the collar around his neck. Then he crossed the room to admire himself in the mirror.

"But I do look nice after I get it on," he said with a twinkle in his eyes.

"Of course you do," said Mrs. Chrysler. "As long as I live, you'll all look nice. I'll teach you to put your best foot forward. It's good for you. Now if everyone's ready, let's go. The people who amount to something in this world are always on time."

Walter buttoned the jacket of his homemade suit. He put his good cap carefully on his head. Then he followed the others out the door.

Walter liked to hear Miss Cartwright play the

organ in church. "I wish the service was all organ music," he thought.

As soon as church was over, Walter and Ed raced home. They reached the house at almost the same time.

Walter put on his old clothes and went to the kitchen. Soon Irene came in to set the table.

"Irene, what are we having for dinner?" Walter asked.

"Wouldn't you like to know?"

"I'll use my nose and find out." Walter opened the oven door. "Aha! Chicken!"

"Yes, and floating island and a white butter cake," Irene added. "I creamed the butter and sugar for the cake myself."

"Girls' work!" Walter teased.

"And boys' work to eat," answered Irene.

Then Mrs. Chrysler came, and the big Sunday dinner was soon on the table.

After dinner Walter got down on the floor

with a big stack of *Scientific American* magazines. He had read them all once or twice or even three times before, but that made no difference. He found them just as interesting now as when he had first read them.

There were pictures and drawings of all sorts of electrical inventions, such as Mr. Bell's telephone and Mr. Edison's lights. There were articles explaining balloons and gliders, darkbox photography and talking machines. Still other articles told about new inventions that were improving the railroads. Best of all, however, were the articles describing new tools and telling how to make them.

It was such things as these that Walter wanted to know. It was such things that he thought and dreamed about.

Today, however, Walter's mind would not stick to scientific matters. When he tried to read, he thought of Miss Cartwright playing the organ at church. He could almost hear the music, now deep and loud like a drum, now high and shrill like a fife.

"I do like music," he thought. "I wish we could hear more of it here in Ellis."

A GREAT IDEA

One evening a few days later the Chryslers were sitting at the kitchen table eating supper. Walter had finished eating and was drinking a glass of milk.

"I've been thinking," he said suddenly during a quiet moment. "I think we ought to have a band in Ellis. It could play on Decoration Day and the Fourth of July."

Mr. Chrysler gave Walter an interested look. "That's a good idea, son," he said. "But I don't know how we'd go about getting one."

"You were a drummer during the War between the States, Dad," Walter reminded him. "Why couldn't you teach some of us how to play in a band? I'd like to learn to beat a drum, and I know some of the other boys would, too."

"The very thing!" exclaimed Mrs. Chrysler.

"Well!" said Mr. Chrysler. "I hadn't thought of that. Do you suppose I could?"

"Sure, Dad," Walter said eagerly. "I know you could. All the boys would like to be in your band. I know they would."

"Well, I'll think about it," said Mr. Chrysler. "The trouble is, I don't know anything but the fife and drum."

"A fife and drum corps would put spirit into any parade," Mrs. Chrysler said. "And spirit is what really counts."

"All right," said Mr. Chrysler. "Get your cap, Walter. We'll go and talk the idea over with some other people in town."

"Yes, sir!" Walter said delightedly.

The next morning Walter ran all the way to school. He rushed up to some of his friends in the schoolyard.

"Joe! Charlie!" he shouted. "Listen, all of you. We're going to have a band. Right here in Ellis. A real band."

"Hey, I like that idea," Joe said.

"Would you like to be in it?" asked Walter.

"You bet I would!" said Joe. "I like music. Who's going to teach us?"

"My father," Walter said. "He asked the G.A.R. if we could practice in their hall."

"Can we?" Charlie asked. More boys were gathering to listen.

"Yes, and what's more, the G.A.R. is going to buy drums for the boys who can't buy their own," Walter said.

"Yip-pee!" The boys threw their caps in the air. "Yip-pee!" they shouted. "Hurrah for the Ellis band!"

102

Within a few weeks ten new drums had been provided for the band. Mr. Chrysler told Walter about them one morning at breakfast.

"Shall I tell the boys to come to the G.A.R. Hall tonight after supper?" Walter asked.

Mr. Chrysler laughed. "You aren't going to waste any time, are you?" He could not hide the fact that he was pleased.

"Yes, tell them to come," he added. "I'll try out everyone who is interested. But tell the boys I can take only those who show some real promise. We have only ten drums."

"Some of them are going to be disappointed," Walter said. "There are more than ten who'd like to be in the band."

Mr. Chrysler looked thoughtful. "We'll see how we get along," he said. "If the drum corps gets off to a good start, perhaps the other boys can play fifes. We'll see."

Walter hurried to school to tell his friends the latest news.

That night after supper all the boys who were interested met at the G.A.R. Hall. Mr. Chrysler tested them to see which boys would make the best drummers. Walter was happy to be chosen among the first ten.

"Now, boys," Mr. Chrysler said, "first of all I'm going to teach you to beat a slow time, or rhythm. When you've learned that, we'll take up a faster, marching time. Now, all together, one—a—two—a—three—a—four!"

"Boom! Boom! Boom! Boom!"

Some of the boys beat too fast. Some beat too slowly. Some drumbeats were too loud. Some were too soft.

"Stop! Stop!" shouted Mr. Chrysler.

"That wasn't music," Walter said with a long face. "That was just noise."

Everyone laughed.

"You can do better than that, boys," Mr. Chrysler said. "Let's try again."

By and by the boys began to get the feel of the drums and the rhythm.

"Now you're doing better," Mr. Chrysler said. "This sounds more like music."

"Dad," Walter said at last, "are we going to beat these drums all evening?"

Mr. Chrysler laid down his baton. "No, the band marches as it plays," he said. "That means you'll have to learn to march in time to the music. First of all, though, you must learn to stand correctly. Put your drums down and get out on the floor."

The boys jumped to their feet and lined up in the hall.

"Now put your heels together, your hands at your sides, your heads up, and your shoulders back," Mr. Chrysler ordered. "Now, march! Left—right—left—right!"

106

At first the boys were confused. They hopped about trying to start on the left foot.

"We're worse than jack rabbits," Walter said with a grin.

Charlie skipped as he tried to get in step. "We're more like a bunch of girls playing hopscotch," he added.

At last the boys went marching around the hall in almost perfect step.

"Good!" said Mr. Chrysler. "When you march like that to the music of your own drums, the whole town will be proud of you."

"That was fun," Joe said as the boys left the hall a short time later.

"Let's see whether we can keep step all the way home," Walter suggested. "Come on. Left—right—left—right!"

The boys fell in step. As they tramped down the dusty street, they took up the count one by one. "Left—right—*left*—*right*—LEFT—RIGHT!"

Surprises for Walter

ONE DAY Walter was in the tool shed working on his model engine. This was the second one he had made. He had thrown the first one away.

He was having trouble with this engine, too. There were so many different parts, and each part had to fit right. He found it necessary to try each part he made to see whether it would work. It was a slow, hard job.

Suddenly he heard Irene calling, "Walter! Oh, Walter! Come here. Dad wants you."

Walter hated to put his work aside, but Irene kept calling.

"Hurry, Walter!"

Walter went to the house. Mr. Chrysler was standing beside a large wooden box which he had just brought home.

"Bring your tools and open this box," Mr. Chrysler said. "It's something for you."

"For me?" said Walter. "But I haven't ordered anything lately."

"I did," said Mr. Chrysler. "Get busy and see what it is. But be careful."

Irene danced around the box. "Hurry, Walter," she said eagerly.

"I can't hurry and be careful, too," he said.

He drew the nails from the top of the packing box and put them in his pocket. Someday he might need those nails. He set the boards aside carefully, too. Someday he might have a good use for them.

When he finally took the packing out of the box, his face lighted up with pleasure. The box contained an expensive snare drum!

Mr. Chrysler smiled. "You're doing so well in our drum corps that I wanted you to have a good drum," he said.

"Thank you, Dad," Walter said.

"This isn't a cheap drum," Mr. Chrysler went on. "Any soldier would be glad to play it in a real army band. You must take care of it."

"Oh, I will! I certainly will!" Walter said happily. "Yes, sir! I'll take good care of it, and I'll practice on it every day."

Walter kept his promise. Every evening, after

he had done the chores, he practiced for an hour. He soon learned to handle the drumsticks with skill.

"Our band is wonderful," he told his mother. "I never knew you could get so much music out of drums. Just drums."

"I'm sure it's wonderful," Mrs. Chrysler said. "I can hardly wait till Decoration Day. Will you play then?"

"Yes, and on the Fourth of July," Walter said.

That winter Walter's father taught a group of boys to play the fife. They thought it a queer little instrument. But they enjoyed playing the tunes which Mr. Chrysler taught them.

After many weeks the drummers and the fife players were ready to practice together. They met as usual in the G.A.R. Hall. After choosing Ed Pearson to be their leader, they practiced the different tunes they had learned for over an hour. Then they practiced marching.

Walter's eyes were dancing as he and his father went home.

"That was easy," he said.

"It was easy because each of you had learned his part perfectly," Mr. Chrysler said. "That's teamwork. I'm quite pleased with all of you. I think people are going to be surprised when they hear our band."

DECORATION DAY

Every year Ellis had a parade on Decoration Day. Every year many people came to town to watch the parade.

At last Decoration Day came. Walter and all the other boys in the band wore new blue shirts and blue overalls, with red handkerchiefs around their necks. They looked like railroad engineers. They were all quite excited.

"I'm glad it's a nice day," Walter said. "Everyone can enjoy our band. We ought to have a big crowd."

The townspeople closed their stores and businesses and gathered along the streets. For miles around farmers hitched their teams to wagons or buckboards and drove in to town. They tied their teams to hitching posts and gathered along the streets with the townspeople.

Cowboys came riding in from the range, shouting and firing their pistols for fun.

The parade assembled on a side street near the business district. At the proper time, Ed Pearson shouted, "At-ten-*tion!*"

Walter and the other boys fell into place.

"One—two—three—four!"

With a great burst of sound the drums began to roll. The boys in the drum corps and all the marchers behind them began to mark time.

Ed Pearson looked back from the head of the parade. "For-ward—*march!*"

The parade had begun.

First came the color guard of four men marching side by side. The two on the outside carried rifles. The two on the inside carried the American flag and the flag of the Kansas militia, or volunteer troops.

Then came Ed Pearson, leading the drum corps and the fifers. The drums rolled. "R-r-um-te-tum! R-r-um-te-tum!" The fifers blew shrilly as if their lives depended on it.

After the fifers came the members of the Grand Army of the Republic. They were all dressed in the blue uniforms which they had worn during the War between the States.

Next came the school children, marching four abreast, each carrying a little flag.

The people watching along the streets cheered with delight. Women waved their handkerchiefs. The men took off their hats.

Mr. Chrysler had told Walter and his friends

in the band to keep straight faces and to act dignified as they marched. Walter found it hard to be dignified. Every time his drumsticks struck his drum, a chill of excitement ran up and down his spine.

The roll of drums and the shrill sound of fifes startled the horses tied to the hitching posts. They suddenly began to pitch and rear with fright. Their neighing added to the noise.

The cowboys ran toward the hitching posts, followed by many farmers. They quieted the horses with strong arms and soothing words.

Meanwhile the parade continued briskly along the streets. As it passed them, all the people cheered and clapped and waved their hats.

After the parade, there were speeches and a community sing. Everyone was eager to honor the soldiers who had fought for their country during the war.

Walter was tired but contented that night.

115

It had been a great day. It had been wonderful to be a part of the celebration. It made him feel good to know that he had helped to make Decoration Day a success.

"THE SWEETEST MUSIC I KNOW"

"Mother, why don't we buy an organ?" Walter asked suddenly one Sunday afternoon. He had been lying on the floor reading a copy of the *Scientific American*.

Mrs. Chrysler looked up from her reading. "An organ!" she exclaimed.

"Yes," said Walter. "I'd like to see Irene play the organ at school or church."

"Oh, I'd love that!" Irene cried.

"But an organ would cost a great deal of money," Mrs. Chrysler said.

Mr. Chrysler had been listening to the conversation. He laid down his book.

"We can buy an organ," he said. "I think
it would be money well spent. I've been thinking for some time about music lessons for Irene,
and an organ is the answer. We'll order one
from Kansas City right away."

When the organ came, Walter helped his father unpack it. Then the whole family gathered
around to admire it.

"My goodness, isn't it fancy!" Irene exclaimed.

Walter nodded. The organ was made of shiny
dark wood and was covered with fancy carving.

There was a rack for music and a shelf and mirror on each side of the rack. There was a high cushioned stool, for the organist to sit on.

"Now that the organ is here, Irene, I think you should start taking lessons at once," Mrs. Chrysler said. "Walter should take them, too."

"Who, me?" cried Walter.

"Certainly," answered his mother. "You, and Ed, too, if he wishes. We all like music in this house. Ed plays his tuba very well, and you're doing well on the drum. But I think you should each know how to play the organ."

Walter sighed, but secretly he was not unhappy. Once a week he and Irene went to the home of Miss Cartwright, the piano teacher. Miss Cartwright did not have an organ, but she gave them a piano lesson. Then they went home and practiced on the organ. Since pianos and organs could be played from the same written music, they got along very well.

At first Walter did not like to play the organ. It was much less exciting than playing a drum in the Ellis drum corps. But after a while he began to enjoy it. It might not be exciting, but it was more musical than drums.

One day after school, Charlie and Joe came to watch him practice.

"Look," Walter said as he pulled out some of the glossy black stops, or handles. "Some stops make the organ play loud. Others make it play soft. Listen."

He began pumping two large flat pedals up and down with his feet. Then he pressed the ivory keys with his fingers. Pleasant sounds came from the organ.

"I think I'd like playing this thing even more if I could watch the bellows work," he said.

But the bellows were carefully enclosed. All Walter could do was to sit on the stool and work the pedals and try to hit the right keys.

One evening several months after he had begun to take organ lessons, Walter came into the house bursting with excitement.

"Guess what, Mother!" he cried. "We're going to start a band, a real band."

"But another band won't teach you anything new, Walter," Mrs. Chrysler said. "The drums will be the same as in the G.A.R. band."

"But I'm not going to play a drum in this band," said Walter. "This band will have all kinds of instruments. I'm going to choose something else."

Mrs. Chrysler shook her head doubtfully. "I don't know whether your father will buy another instrument for you or not," she said.

Walter laughed. "Mother, have you forgotten about the money that I've earned?"

"My goodness, yes, I have," said Mrs. Chrysler. "I should have remembered, because you worked hard for that money. Well, go ahead and get a musical instrument. You couldn't spend your money for anything better."

After much thought, Walter decided to buy a clarinet. He ordered it by mail from Kansas City. He was glad that he had saved enough money to buy the clarinet himself. It made him feel grown-up, like his father and his brother.

In a short time he learned to play the clarinet as well as he played the organ or the drum.

"You're quite a musician, Walter," his mother said one night after hearing him play.

"Oh, I don't know," Walter said. "I like music. I enjoy playing in the band with the rest of the fellows. But the prettiest music I know is a locomotive's whistle."

New Ventures

ONE SPRING evening when Walter was fourteen the Chrysler family was eating supper. Supper was later than usual, because Mr. Chrysler had been late getting home.

Mrs. Chrysler piled Walter's plate high with food, and Walter started to eat. Presently he stopped and looked at his father.

"Dad, did you know the Johnsons over on the next street are starting to build a new house?" he asked.

Mr. Chrysler raised his eyes from his plate. "No, I didn't know it," he said. "But what has that to do with us?"

"Seems to me something was once said about the Chryslers building a new house."

"Yes, that's right," said Ed. "Whatever became of that idea?"

Mr. Chrysler ate the last crumb of his pie. He pushed back his plate.

"Well, I'm ready to build a new house this summer," he said.

Walter sprang to his feet. His chair fell over. "I'll help, Dad!" he shouted.

"I'm counting on that," said Mr. Chrysler with a smile. He was glad to see Walter interested in such a large undertaking.

"I hope it will be a big house," Ed said.

"I hope it will have a big front porch," Irene added eagerly.

"Don't you think we'd better build the kind of a house your mother wants?" Mr. Chrysler asked. "After all, she's the one who will have to take care of it."

"Mother, what kind of house do you want?" Walter asked. "We'll build anything you want, even if it's a palace. Won't we, Dad?"

Mr. Chrysler smiled.

"Yes, because every American's home is his palace," he said. "That's one of the best things about America. We're all free men, and our homes are ours."

He turned to Mrs. Chrysler. "Mother, what do you want your new palace to be like?"

"Oh, dear me," said Mrs. Chrysler. "I'll have to think it over for a few days."

"Very well," said Mr. Chrysler. "In the meantime I'll order lumber, nails, and shingles."

One evening a short time later, Mr. Chrysler brought home a large sheet of heavy brown paper. After supper he spread the paper on the kitchen table.

"What are you going to do now, Dad?" Walter asked, watching him curiously.

"I'm going to draw plans for the new house,"
Mr. Chrysler said. "I want all of you to help—
especially Mother."

Mr. Chrysler got his steel square, a ruler, and
a sharp pencil. Then the family sat down around
the table to plan the new house.

WALTER BECOMES A BUILDER

One evening a few weeks later Walter went
with his father to the workshop in the back
yard. Summer vacation had started and Walter
had plenty of time on his hands. He was eager
to find something to do.

"When are we going to start building the new
house?" Walter asked.

"The lumber will be delivered tomorrow,"
said Mr. Chrysler.

"Good!" said Walter. "I'm ready."

He went to the corner of the shop which his

father had fixed for him. He looked at his tools hanging above his workbench.

"I have a good square and a hammer," he said. "But I'll need other tools to build a house."

"Yes, you have a good start on a tool collection," Mr. Chrysler said. "You've done a good job on some of those you've made, son."

"I'll need a saw, though," Walter said.

Mr. Chrysler took a small saw from among his own tools.

"Here, you may have this one," he said.

"Thank you, Dad," Walter said. "I'll take good care of it."

"If I didn't know that, I wouldn't be giving it to you," Mr. Chrysler said. He crossed the shed to look at Walter's workbench. In one corner were scraps of metal and short pieces of small pipe. In the center of the bench was Walter's unfinished locomotive.

"Is this your engine, Walter?" Mr. Chrysler

127

asked. He picked up one of the pieces and studied it carefully.

"Yes," Walter replied.

"How's it coming along?"

"Slow," Walter sighed. "It's a lot more work than I thought it would be. Each piece has to be just the right size and shape or it won't work. I think before I go any farther I'll draw some plans, the way you did for the house."

"That's a good idea," Mr. Chrysler said. He gave Walter an encouraging slap on the shoulder. "Building an engine that will run is a big order. But keep on trying, Walter. The men who have done big things in this world are the ones who are willing to do the hard things."

The next day Walter and his father set the stakes to show where the corners of the new house were to be. They measured the corners to make sure that they were square and marked lines to show where the foundation was to be dug.

128

"This is fun!" Walter exclaimed. "I can see right now that what I've learned in school is going to help in building this house."

"Of course it will," said Mr. Chrysler. "I never had a chance to go to high school, as you and Ed have. But I know this. A man must know exactly what he's doing if he wants to build something useful. I've had to learn by guesswork. That's the hard way. Now you're learning facts. Facts will help you to know how to go ahead on your job."

The new house had to be built at odd times. Mr. Chrysler had his regular runs on the railroad. Walter often was busy selling things. Ed could help only after he came from work in the machine shop. But every day they managed to do a little. Even Mrs. Chrysler and Irene did what they could to help.

Finally the house was finished. It was two stories high and had a front porch. Its size pleased Ed and its porch pleased Irene. Everything about it pleased Mrs. Chrysler.

"My, but it's nice," she said.

"I think it is, too," said Walter. "But I wish we had a white picket fence around the yard. A fence would look nice, too."

"Would you like to build one, son?" asked Mr. Chrysler with a smile.

Walter grinned with delight. "I'll nail every picket on as straight as—as—well, I'll put them on straight!"

When Walter finally finished the fence, the family came out to admire it.

"Not bad, Walter," Ed said, clapping him on the shoulder. "I hate to say this to a young fellow like you, but you did a good job."

Walter stepped back to look at the fence. He whistled softly and grinned. "If that's what you think, I guess it's all right for me to admire it, too, isn't it?" he said.

Every morning before school Walter pumped a tank full of water. He had to make the pump handle go up and down many times to fill the tank completely.

"I'll bet I've pumped a million gallons of water," he declared one day. "Three cows and four horses drink a lot of water."

"Yes, they do," Mr. Chrysler agreed. "And I know how tiresome it is to pump water."

Walter stepped to the tank and rinsed his face and arms in the cool water.

"Well, then why don't we figure out something that will pump water for us?" he asked. "The *Scientific American* tells how to build engines and windmills and——"

Mr. Chrysler held up his hand. "Stop right there," he said with a chuckle. "Your ideas are coming too fast. Let me think about it."

One evening a few weeks later Mr. Chrysler

131

said, "Walter, how would you like to help me build a windmill tower?"

Walter, who was lying on the floor with a magazine, sprang to his feet.

"A windmill tower!" he shouted. "I'd like that fine, just fine!"

Walter whistled happily as he did his chores that evening. A windmill would save him a lot of time and work. He had seen a few on farms out in the country, but nobody in Ellis had one. In fact, nobody in Ellis thought a windmill was worth building.

When Walter told his friends about the windmill that night at band practice, they just looked at him.

"Why do you want a windmill?" one said.

"Why, we'll make it work for us, of course," Walter said.

Walter helped his father draw plans for the windmill tower.

"We'll build the tower ourselves," said Mr. Chrysler. "But we must order the windmill from a factory in the East."

School had started before Mr. Chrysler found time to start the tower. Every evening after school Walter hurried home to help. He sawed boards where Mr. Chrysler had marked them. He carried boards and nails here and there where they were needed. He held saws and hammers and planes for Mr. Chrysler.

At last the tower was finished and the mill wheel arrived from the factory. The next day Mr. Chrysler climbed up to the platform on top of the tower. With a rope he pulled up some pulleys, which he fastened to the platform. Then Walter and the neighbors pulled the heavy wheel and tail up to the top of the tower.

"Tomorrow is Saturday," Mr. Chrysler said when they had finished. "By tomorrow noon we'll have this windmill ready to work for us."

SATURDAY AND ITS PROMISE

Walter was so eager to see the windmill work that he thought Saturday would never come. But it finally did.

As soon as Walter had finished breakfast, he hurried out to get his friends.

"Come on, fellows," he said. "Let's sit on the fence and watch the mill work."

He and his friends lined up on the top board of the pasture fence and waited. It was a bright autumn day. A steady wind chased little white clouds across the sky. The boys could feel it on their faces.

Carefully Mr. Chrysler raised a long lever at the bottom of the tower. This loosened a wire cable that controlled the mill. The tail of the mill swung out and pointed away from the wheel. The wind caught the tail and turned the mill around until the wheel faced the wind. Then the wind caught the blades of the wheel and the wheel began to turn.

As the wheel turned, a long rod running from the wheel to the pump below went up and down, up and down. Suddenly water began to flow from the pump to the tank where the cows came to drink. The wind was pumping water.

"Hurrah!" shouted Walter. "Now I won't have to pump water any more."

"Hurrah! Hurrah!" shouted the other boys. They began to wish that their fathers would buy windmills, too.

Every morning after that Walter started the pump when he went out to feed the horses and cows. Usually by the time he had finished, the tank was full. Sometimes he sat on the fence and watched the windmill work. He studied the wheel, the tail, the cogs, and the gears and rods of which it was made. He wanted to learn how it was made and why it worked. It was a machine, like his father's engine, and he wanted to understand machines.

One day Walter found his parents standing between the windmill and the house. They were looking thoughtfully from one to the other.

"What are you figuring on now, Dad?" he asked, hurrying forward.

"Running water," said Mr. Chrysler.

"Running water!" Walter shouted. "Why, if

136

we had running water we could have a bathroom. No one in Ellis has a bathroom."

"No, there's not a bathroom in Ellis," said Mrs. Chrysler. "But I'd be mighty proud if you and your father could put a new bathroom in our house."

"We'll do it!" said Walter and his father together. "Just wait and see."

Walter helped his father make all the measurements. He helped to plan a water tank and a system of pipes and valves, and to put them in. He helped build the tub of wood and line it with sheets of bright copper. He helped make it watertight.

When the work was finished, Walter brought his mother to see it. "There!" he said. "Now when we come home tired and dirty, we can get cleaned up in a jiffy. I'll bet when the neighbors see this, all of them will want windmills and bathtubs, too."

"They may want them, but I doubt whether many will go to the trouble to get them," said Mr. Chrysler. "Not many boys are willing to work as hard as you are, son."

Walter smiled at his father. "This wasn't work, Dad," he replied. "It was fun. I enjoyed working both on the house and the windmill. Each day I learned how to do something different with tools, and that is what I want most."

Walter's New World

"You know, Mother," Walter said one day after he had started to high school, "Ellis is growing so fast nowadays that I think I could find a regular job somewhere."

"What could you do?" asked Mrs. Chrysler.

"I don't know," Walter said. "But I'm sure I could find something."

"Well, Walter, the thing to do is to try," Mrs. Chrysler replied.

A few days later Walter overheard a neighbor talking to his mother about Mrs. Henderson, whose husband ran the store.

"I feel sorry for Mrs. Henderson," the neighbor said. "She's up at dawn, washing, ironing, baking, mending, and taking care of her children. And as if that weren't enough, Mr. Henderson wants her to help in the store. It's 'Sarah, do this,' or 'Sarah, do that.' 'Sarah, keep the store while I deliver a barrel of flour.' That man ought to hire help."

"Yes, he should be able to use a big strong boy," said Mrs. Chrysler. She looked to see where Walter was. But Walter was already on his way to Mr. Henderson's store.

He was still running when he entered the door. Inside, several customers were waiting to be taken care of. Barrels and boxes were stacked everywhere, waiting to be opened.

"Don't you need some help, Mr. Henderson?" Walter asked.

"I surely do," Mr. Henderson answered without looking around. "Grab that hatchet on the counter and open those barrels."

140

Walter found the hatchet and went to work. When evening came, he said, "Did I do all right today, Mr. Henderson?"

"Yes, you did, Walter," Mr. Henderson said.

"Then how about a regular job? I think you could use me every day."

"You're right, absolutely right," said Mr. Henderson. "I could use you. I'll pay you ten dollars a month."

Ten dollars a month! Walter could hardly be-

141

lieve what he had heard. That was wealth! When he told his mother what Mr. Henderson had said, she was just as pleased as he was.

Walter did well in the store. He spent most of his time unpacking and delivering groceries. But when people came in, he was always eager and willing to help them. He was always glad when someone asked for tools or other things in the hardware section.

Most of the groceries were kept in barrels and boxes behind a long counter. There were dried beans, rice, sugar, dried fruits, coffee, and many other things. When anyone wanted something, Walter filled a sack from the proper box or barrel and weighed the sack on the scales.

"Always give just a little bit more than people pay for," Mr. Henderson told him. "Customers like to get good measure as well as good food. If we give them good measure, they'll come back again and again."

Many of the customers did not have a horse and carriage or wagon to take their groceries home. Then Walter put the groceries in a two-wheeled cart and delivered them himself. Day after day he went about town, pushing the cart down the street ahead of him.

School, the band, the drum corps, and his job left Walter little time for fun. He did not play marbles in front of the station much any more. He spent little time in the freight yards, watching the trains and talking to their crews. He spent little time studying the locomotives.

Just the same, he never forgot the railroad. If a train whistled in the distance, he heard it and knew what its whistle meant. He knew when every train was supposed to reach Ellis and when it was supposed to leave. He knew every engineer and fireman by name.

One day a train blocked the street as Walter was delivering groceries. Pushing his cart close to the engine, he studied the big drive wheels and the drive shafts connecting the wheels to the pistons. He looked at the bell and whistle and listened to the hiss of escaping steam. He felt a rain of tiny cinders as smoke puffed from the stack.

He smiled happily. He enjoyed bands and marbles, but this was what really interested him. "Nothing beats a steam engine," he thought.

When the train pulled out, Walter went on delivering groceries. But he was counting the years until he could start to work on the railroad himself. He wanted that day to come more than anything else in the world.

ICE SKATES AND A SHOTGUN

The following winter heavy rains fell and flooded the countryside. Then cold winds swept down from the north.

One Sunday afternoon Walter went with his friends to look at the ice on the creek that flowed through Ellis.

"One more cold day and we ought to have good skating," Joe McMahon said.

"Yip-pee!" shouted one of the boys. "I'm going home to polish up my skates."

"I'm going home to ask my father to buy me a pair," said another boy.

Walter listened to them. He wanted skates, but he did not care to spend his own money or to ask his father to buy him skates.

He made a sudden decision. "I'm going to make my skates," he said.

"Make skates!" The boys shouted with laughter. "You can't make skates."

"Who wants homemade skates anyway?" someone asked. "I don't."

Walter said nothing. He went home, found a bright piece of steel in his father's shop, and went to work. When the skates were finished, they did not look clumsy or homemade. They were just as bright and sharp and fitted him just as well as any he could have bought.

Walter took his new skates to the creek. This time the boys did not laugh.

"Why, they're all right," Joe said.

"Yes, they're just as good as mine," said Charlie in surprise.

"Of course they are," Walter said indignantly. "I wouldn't have tried to make them if I hadn't known I could."

One day a few weeks later Walter was watching his father clean and polish his shotgun.

"I think I'll make a shotgun," he said suddenly. "I'd like to have one of my own."

Mr. Chrysler looked up from his work. "I'm sure you can make a good shotgun if you try, Walter. You're becoming quite a mechanic these days. I'm proud of you."

Walter was pleased to hear his father say that. He enjoyed making things.

Mrs. Chrysler paused in her knitting.

"I've an idea you can make just about anything you wish, Walter," she said. "Of course, I used to worry about you some. You always spent so much time watching anything on wheels. And you pored over the *Scientific American* when you should have been asleep. But I can see now that you weren't wasting time. You were figuring things out for yourself."

Walter laughed sheepishly.

"When I get to thinking about something interesting, I forget everything else," he said. "I can't help it."

Before he started to make the shotgun, Walter studied his father's gun carefully. He took it apart and measured and made a drawing of each part. He wanted to know just exactly how the gun was made.

Ed came to the kitchen one night as he was working on his drawings.

"What are you doing that for?" he asked with a twinkle in his eyes. "It seems like a waste of time to me."

Walter's dark eyes flashed. "Waste of time! You should know better than that, Ed Chrysler. You work with plans all the time. If I didn't have plans, how would I know what size or shape to make each part?"

When he finished his plans, Walter hunted materials to make the gun. Then, before starting to work, he studied his father's gun and his own drawings again and again. He wanted the gun to be perfect.

When Walter told his friends that he was making a shotgun, they laughed again.

"Walter, you're crazy," one of them said. "Don't you know that gun could blow your head off if it isn't just right?"

"We know you made skates, Walter," said another. "But a gun's different!"

"Oh, be still!" said Joe McMahon. "You know Walter can make a gun if he tries."

Walter made the gun. It was a good gun, too, and worked as well as any that he might have bought in a store.

Mr. Chrysler clapped Walter on the shoulder when he saw the gun. "Good work, son," he said. "I knew you could do it. You have a gift for working with tools. You have something else, too, that is just as important, and maybe even more important. You like to do things right."

"Thank you, Dad," Walter said, smiling with pleasure. "I think half the fun in making things is in making them right."

They were standing in the workshop, where Walter had just finished putting the gun together. Now he turned to look at a pile of things on one corner of the bench. There were several wheels, some shiny bars or rods, a long cylinder, and several smaller cylinders.

"That's why I've never finished making a model engine," he said. "I can't get it right."

Mr. Chrysler picked up the parts and studied them carefully. "What's the trouble?"

Walter sighed. "I don't know, Dad. I guess I just don't know enough about engines. This is the third one I've tried to make, and it isn't any better than the others."

He turned one of the wheels over in his hand. Then he looked at his father again. "When I finish school I'm going to be a machinist, like Ed," he said. "I'm going to learn all there is to know about steam engines."

SEVENTEEN

It was May, 1892, and Commencement Day at Ellis High School. All the boys and girls in the senior class were excited, for this was an important day in their lives.

The commencement exercises were to be held in the G.A.R. Hall. The girls had decorated the hall with flowers. The boys had placed rows of chairs and benches in the hall. The exercises were to include music and speaking, and each pupil in the class was to receive a diploma.

There was a good deal of bustle and excitement in the Chrysler house that day. Walter was seventeen and a member of the graduating class. He and his family were getting dressed to go to the exercises.

Walter stood in the middle of the kitchen, twisting his neck and running one finger around his stiff collar.

"I wish I didn't have to wear this collar," he said. "I'm mighty uncomfortable."

He leaned down and brushed off his shoes. They were the first patent leather shoes he had ever had. He put on the coat of his new Sunday suit. Then he looked at himself in a mirror.

"You look nice, Walter," his mother said.

"I do at that, don't I?" Walter grinned.

Mrs. Chrysler went to the door, which Mr. Chrysler opened for her. "Come, children," she said. "We mustn't be late."

Walter followed his mother and sister out the door. Then he and Ed and his father walked behind them along the new wooden sidewalks.

There were other families on the sidewalk, too, all going to the exercises. There were girls in new white dresses and boys in stiff shoes and new Sunday suits. There were proud parents and older brothers and sisters, and noisy younger brothers and sisters. Horses kicked up clouds of dust as they trotted down the street toward the hall.

All the people filed in slowly to find their seats. Walter and the other seniors took their places on a platform at one end of the hall.

Presently the principal rose and the commencement exercises began. There were songs and recitations by some members of the class. There were speeches by others. Finally the principal awarded each member of the class a diploma.

Walter listened closely when the program began, but his thoughts soon began to wander. This was an important day in his life, he knew. While it might be his last day of school, it was really just a beginning.

Now there lay before him the exciting world of grown men—his father's world of locomotives, his brother Ed's world of machines. The more he thought about that world, and what he might do in it, the more excited he became.

"I wish I could go to work right now," he thought. "There are so many things I want to learn. There are so many things I have to know!"

Working for
the Railroad

WALTER RAN down the street. His long legs pumped hard, and his heels rapped loudly on the boards of the sidewalk.

"Joe!" he yelled. "Wait a minute, Joe!"

Joe McMahon looked back, then waited until Walter caught up with him.

"Guess what?" Walter panted. "I have a job in the shops! I'm going to be a sweep boy!"

"A sweep boy!" Joe said in surprise. "Well, they *are* making you start at the bottom!"

"I don't care," Walter said, smiling. "It isn't being an apprentice machinist, but it's a start in the shops. That's what I want."

"Well, good luck," Joe said. "Of course, I know I don't need to wish you that."

Walter laughed. "Thanks, Joe," he said. "I'm going to be the best sweep boy the Union Pacific ever had. But right now I'd better be a good grocery clerk. I haven't told Mr. Henderson yet."

Mr. Henderson was sad when Walter told him that he was leaving.

"I don't know what I'll do without you, Walter," he said. "You've been a good clerk and I hate to lose you. I tell you what. I have a good business now. If you'll stay with me, I'll raise your pay."

"Thank you, Mr. Henderson," Walter replied. "It's mighty fine of you to make such an offer. If I wanted to run a store, I would stay. But I don't. I want to be a machinist."

"Well, wherever you go and whatever you do, boy, I wish you luck. And remember this—

honest weight and good measure work everywhere, not just in the grocery business."

"I believe that," Walter said with a smile. "I won't forget it."

Walter was used to hard work. But for the first few days, pushing his heavy broom over the dirty wood floors of the shop made him tired. In addition to sweeping, he had to carry heavy pipes from the engines to sheds outside, where they were cleaned. Being a sweep boy was not an easy job, he learned.

Walter did everything he was told to do. Sometimes he saw things to do that were not part of his regular job. He did those, too.

Every morning after breakfast he rushed over to the shops. He always tried to be early so that he would have time to look around.

After a while he learned to plan his work so he could spend time in the locomotive shop. He watched the engines being taken apart and put back together again. It wasn't long before he knew where each part of an engine belonged and what its purpose was. Then his job as sweep boy grew more interesting.

"You know, Mother," he said one evening, "my job is fun. Each morning when I wake up I wonder what I'll learn during the day."

"You'll learn something worth while every day," Mrs. Chrysler said. "You can't help learning if you keep your eyes open."

THE PROMOTION

Shortly before his eighteenth birthday, Walter was called into the master mechanic's office. The master mechanic's name was Esterbrook.

"Walter," he said, "I've been watching you. You're too good a worker to be sweeping floors. I understand you want to be a machinist."

"Yes, sir." Walter could hardly speak.

"Well, then, would you like it if I made you an apprentice machinist?"

"Like it!" Walter exclaimed.

Mr. Esterbrook smiled. "I thought you'd say something like that. Well, it's settled then. Of course, we'll have to straighten out a few things first. For one thing, I can pay you only ten cents an hour as an apprentice. That's less than you're making now as a sweep boy."

"Oh, that doesn't matter," Walter said cheerfully. "I'll work for nothing if I have to." He was grinning from ear to ear. Nothing had ever pleased him more, not even his first ride on his father's engine. He had taken his first step toward success.

"Of course, you know that I'll have to have your father's permission for you to become an apprentice," Mr. Esterbrook said.

"I'll ask him tonight, " Walter said.

Walter hurried home that night after work.

He was eager to tell his mother the news, and even more eager to tell his father.

Mr. Chrysler listened soberly to Walter's eager words.

"I'm glad that Mr. Esterbrook thinks so well of you, son," he said. "Still, I wish you would get some more education."

"I've been thinking about that, Dad," Walter said. "Do you remember those correspondence courses we saw advertised in a magazine not so long ago? I thought I might study some of those at night."

"If you're willing to do that, I'll be glad to let you become an apprentice," Mr. Chrysler said.

So Walter went to work as an apprentice. Soon he began to study mechanics and engineering by mail. He received the lessons from the school by mail. After he studied them, he wrote the answers and sent them back by mail.

"This is good, Walter," his mother said one

night. "During the day you learn to work with your hands. At night you learn to work with your head. You will be a great man some day."

Walter was sitting at the kitchen table with the latest copy of the *Scientific American* open before him. He was so busy reading that he hardly heard what his mother said.

Presently he said, "Dad, this article says that a man named Elwood Haynes has built a horseless carriage. It is run by a small, two-horsepower gasoline engine."

"I reckon those gasoline engines are going to be as useful as steam engines some day," Mr. Chrysler said thoughtfully.

"I don't see how they could be," said Mrs. Chrysler, looking over Walter's shoulder.

"I'd certainly like to see this," Walter said. "I'd like to see how it's made and to find out exactly what makes it go."

"You'd soon figure it out," said Mrs. Chrysler.

163

"And wouldn't I look stylish riding in one of those!" She and Mr. Chrysler laughed.

"I couldn't drive it for you," he said. "I'd need a track. I guess I'd better stick to steam engines and railroad tracks."

Walter hardly heard them. He was reading the article carefully.

"Someday I'll know," he thought. "Someday I'll know all there is to know about locomotives and horseless carriages."

MAKING HIS OWN TOOLS

One evening Walter came home covered with grease and soot. He stood in the kitchen doorway, smiling.

"Howdy, ladies," he said. "What's for supper? I'm so hungry I could eat a whole buffalo!"

Irene stood at the table with the silverware in her hands and stared at her brother.

"Walter, you're a sight!" she cried. "Where have you been?"

Walter's white teeth and the whites of his eyes gleamed through the dirt.

"I've been down in the roundhouse pits," he said. "Under an engine, and inside it, too."

"And you like that kind of work?"

"Like it? I love it! I learned how to repair an engine's valves today."

Mrs. Chrysler laughed. "And learning made you so hungry you could eat a buffalo. Well, I'm afraid the days of buffalo meat are over. But I have plenty of beef."

Finally Walter was ready to eat. He was still thinking and talking about his work.

"I need more tools," he said. "I think I'll make them myself. I can copy tools that belong to fellows at the shop. Or I'll figure out how to make them from pictures in a catalog."

Irene looked at him in admiration.

"There isn't anything you won't try to make, is there?" she said.

"Not if it's something I need," he answered.

Walter started on his tools in his first spare time. The first thing he made was a pair of calipers. He showed the calipers to his father.

"Look, Dad," he said. "These calipers will measure the diameter of anything up to four inches. They'll be a big help to me."

Mr. Chrysler examined the calipers. "Nice work, Walter," he said. "I suppose you'll make more now. You'll need larger ones, I know."

Walter laughed.

"Oh, yes," he said. "Just wait till you see the big ones I've planned. They'll be as long as my arm. They're going to be the granddaddy of all calipers."

It was part of Walter's training to work with the top mechanic from time to time. One day Walter was watching him measure the depth of a hole in a piece of iron. The man was using a piece of wire. He put the wire in the hole and set his thumbnail on the wire even with the top of the hole. Then he measured the distance from his thumbnail to the end of the wire.

"That isn't the best way to measure the depth of a hole, is it?" Walter said.

"I can make a fitting this way that won't be off more than a sixteenth of an inch," the mechanic said. "Can you think of a better way of doing the job?"

Walter's face grew red, but he went on.

"A depth gauge would make an exact measurement," he said. "It wouldn't be off at all. You wouldn't need to do so much filing and cutting if you used a depth gauge."

"There isn't a depth gauge this side of the Mississippi River," the mechanic said.

That night Walter went to his shop. "I'm going to make a depth gauge," he told himself.

He began measuring and sawing and shaping some pieces of steel. When he had finished his work, he showed it to his father.

Mr. Chrysler studied it thoughtfully. "It's a nice piece of work, Walter," he said at last. "But just what is it?"

"It's a depth gauge," Walter said. "And according to one of the mechanics, it's the only one west of the Mississippi River."

After that Walter made a number of useful tools which the workmen needed in the shops. Whenever he made something, he showed it to an old carpenter with whom he had become friendly lately.

"I've learned to mark my initials on my tools," he said one day. "See, I use an acid that burns the letters into the steel."

The old man saw the letters *W P C* on several of Walter's tools. He rubbed his fingers over the letters.

"That's a good idea," he said. "Where did you get it, Walter?"

"In the *Scientific American*," Walter said. "Maybe my tools won't get lost so easily now. Some day when I get around to it I'm going to make a tool chest."

The old man's eyes began to twinkle. "I've heard you say that before," he said.

He went to one corner of his shop and uncovered a stout tool chest. "Look here," he said. "I've made this for you in my spare time."

Walter was so surprised that he could think of nothing to say.

"Oh! Well! Thank you, thank you!" he finally gasped. "Thank you very much. It's surely a fine chest. I'll keep it always!"

Then he painted his name on the chest in large letters: W. P. Chrysler.

THE MODEL ENGINE

After Walter had been an apprentice for a while, he decided that he finally knew enough to make a model of a steam engine. This time he was going to make one that would really run.

He looked around in the junk heaps at the railroad shops. He found a thick piece of iron. It was just the right size for the body of his engine. He took the piece of iron home to his own workbench.

He decided to make a model of his father's

engine. First of all, he measured every part of the engine so that he would know how large it was. Then he figured out how large each part on the model should be. He drew plans until he knew just what he had to do.

He worked slowly and carefully. For many weeks all his spare time was given to shaping and finishing the parts for his engine.

Finally the work was finished, and he had a perfect, twenty-eight-inch model of his father's locomotive. Walter invited Charlie and Joe over to see it.

"It's a beauty, Walter," Joe said. "I never thought you could actually make an engine with pressure valves, throttle, and all."

"It's complete," Walter said proudly.

"Yes, even to the bell and cowcatcher," Charlie added.

"Dad is going to help me lay a track for it tomorrow," Walter said.

171

Almost everyone in Ellis came to the Chrysler house during the next few days. Everybody wanted to see the little engine go puffing along the track which Walter and his father had laid out around the yard.

"Isn't it a dandy?" someone said.

"Why, it's perfect!"

"It runs like a real engine!"

Crowds of little boys looked on in wide-eyed wonder, too.

Ed was proud of Walter. "Walter, I told you a few years ago that you couldn't build an engine like this. I can see now how mistaken I was. I expect to see you build a locomotive for the railroad someday."

"Maybe I will," Walter said thoughtfully. "This country needs bigger and better engines."

Walter watched his little engine come to the end of its track. He stood with his hands in his pockets and whistled softly to himself. Plans for a bigger and better engine were crowding into his mind.

He heard the whistle of a freight train entering town. He could tell that the train was heavily loaded and that the engine was puffing under strain.

Suddenly he heard his father speaking. "You're a railroadman now, Walter. You've got your job cut out for you, helping to develop better railroad service for this country."

"I'll try," Walter replied. "I have some ideas that I'd certainly like to develop."

"I'm sure you have," said Mr. Chrysler. "And that's what is making this country grow—men with ideas. It's a free country, Walter. Keep your ideas growing."

An American
Workman

ONE DAY two men were having lunch in the dining room of a men's club in the city of Pittsburgh. One was dark-haired and fairly young. The other was somewhat older. The older man was Superintendent of Motive Power for a large eastern railroad. He was in charge of all the railroad's locomotives.

"Listen, Walter," he said, "I want an engine that will haul twelve Pullman cars up a low hill at sixty miles an hour. I want twenty-five of them. Now go back to your office and figure out how much you'll charge to make them."

"All right, Mr. Turner," said the younger man.

When lunch was over, the younger man hurried to his offices at the American Locomotive Company. This company was one of the country's largest makers of locomotives. The young man was Walter Chrysler, the manager of the company's Pittsburgh works.

Once at his desk, Walter called several assistants into his office. He told them what he wanted and asked them to figure what the locomotives would cost.

"Let's do it quickly," he said. "Turner doesn't want to wait."

When the others were gone, Walter sat at his desk for a while, thinking. Then he rose and went to the windows to look out.

Smoke and heavy gray clouds darkened the sky. Across the river he could see the glowing fires and tall chimneys of a steel mill. To his right, on the near side of the river, he could see the red glare of his own foundry. There molten

iron was being made into wheels, pistons, iron
sheets, and other heavy parts for locomotives.

As he stood at the window, someone entered
the room behind him.

"Mr. Chrysler?"

Walter turned. It was his secretary.

"There's a gentleman waiting to see you," she
said. "He says he's an old friend of yours. His
name is Keagy."

176

"Charlie Keagy!" Walter cried, delighted. "I should say he is an old friend! Send him in."

He was waiting at the door with outstretched hand when Charlie Keagy reached it.

"Charlie! Am I glad to see you! How are things in Ellis? How's your family? What have you heard from Joe McMahon? What have you heard——"

"Wait! Wait!" Charlie Keagy held up his hands. "One question at a time, Walter, please."

He studied Walter with a smile. Then he said, "It's been a long time since you and I saw each other, Walter. Let's see. It must have been the day you and Della Forker were married."

Walter laughed. "That *was* a long time ago. We have two daughters and a son now."

"How long have you and Della been in Pittsburgh?" Charlie asked.

"Several years," Walter answered. "We came here after I left my job as Superintendent of

Power for the Chicago Great Western Railroad. We were living in Iowa then."

"Most people spend their whole lives in one town," Charlie said. "But you and Della have lived in many places."

"I was a regular rolling stone for a while," Walter laughed. "After I left Ellis I worked in Kansas, Wyoming, Colorado, Utah, Idaho, and then Texas.

"I was working in Salt Lake City when I came back to Ellis to marry Della. I became a master mechanic in Salt Lake City. We went from there to Colorado, and from Colorado to Texas, and then to Iowa."

"Why did you move around so much?"

"I was restless," Walter said. "I wanted to learn. Besides, each job seemed to be a little better than the last one."

"And now instead of repairing locomotives, you're making new ones."

"Yes," Walter said, "and I'm happier, too. You know, I always did like to make things."

"How well I remember!" Charlie laughed. "Skates, tools, a gun—and a model engine. When you made that engine you didn't know you'd be making real ones someday, did you?"

"No," Walter said. "But even in those days I wanted to make something. I get a thrill and a kind of satisfaction from making things that I can't get in any other way."

He paused and looked thoughtfully out the window at the smoky valley. Then he added, "I loved working for the railroad. But I love manufacturing even more."

WALTER BUILDS AN AUTOMOBILE

One day in 1924 a group of people were gathered in the lobby of the Commodore Hotel in New York City. In the center of the group was

a man, and beside the man was an automobile. Resting one hand proudly on the fender of the automobile, the man was answering questions.

"Is it true that this car will go seventy miles an hour?" someone asked.

"Yes," the man answered.

"And it has six cylinders?"

"Yes."

The man who asked the questions studied the gleaming engine under the open hood. He ran his hand lightly over the soft upholstery. He looked at the name plate on the radiator—a red seal with a silver wing on each side and the name CHRYSLER printed on the seal.

"It's quite an automobile, Mr. Chrysler," he said. "But isn't a high-powered engine like this something for racing cars? No other companies make such an engine."

Walter Chrysler laughed. "They would if they could. No one has been able to design an engine

181

like this and make it cheaply enough to put it in a passenger car. That's the only reason the other companies haven't done it."

"Well, then, doesn't it make your car rather expensive? What is the price going to be?"

Walter shook his head, smiled, and moved on. He wasn't ready to answer that question yet. He went to a man who was standing at one side of the lobby.

"Joe," he said, "renting this lobby was a good idea. We're getting a better show here than we'd have had at the National Automobile Show at Grand Central Palace."

"People like the car," Joe said. "They're interested, no doubt about that. I could take orders right now if you'd tell me the price."

Walter laughed. "That's what everyone wants to know. Well, I guess the company's sales manager has a right to know the price of his own product. Here."

He wrote a figure on a card and handed it to Joe Fields, then walked away. Joe read the card, frowned thoughtfully for a moment, then suddenly grinned.

"The price is high," he said to himself. "But not too high for what people will get."

Later that evening Walter Chrysler was talking to a reporter from a New York newspaper.

"Mr. Chrysler, how did you get into the automobile business?" the reporter asked. "Didn't you make locomotives once?"

"Yes," Walter said, "but locomotives and automobiles are really the same business—the transportation business. I've always been in the transportation business."

They were sitting on the balcony overlooking the lobby and the crowd that had gathered to inspect the new automobile.

"Actually," Walter added with a smile, "I became interested in automobiles the day I bought my first one in 1908. It was red and white, and, my, was I proud of it! I took it apart and put it together several times before I tried to drive it. I wanted to know just how it was made and why it ran."

"And you found out?"

"Oh, yes! And I learned something else, too. The automobile is just as promising today as the railroad was back in my father's day. The railroads helped to build our country then. Today the automobile is helping to build it.

"Well, I became interested in the automobile business. When I was offered a job as works manager of the Buick Company, I jumped at the chance. I became president of Buick, then left to run another company. Then, a few years ago, my friends and I bought the Maxwell Company, and here we are."

"I understand it won't be the Maxwell Company much longer," said the reporter.

184

"That's right. We're changing the name to the Chrysler Corporation. And believe me, young man, I'm prouder of that name than I am of anything else except ——"

"Except what, sir?"

"My wife, my daughters, and my two sons."

"IT REALLY SCRAPES THE SKY"

There are many tall buildings in the city of New York. It is famous for them. One of the tallest and most beautiful is on Fifth Avenue, in the heart of the city. It was one of the first buildings that could truthfully be called "skyscrapers." It is known as the Chrysler Building.

One day a boy named Danny Wills and his father paid the Chrysler Building a visit. Danny lived in Iowa and had always wanted to go to the top of a skyscraper. He wanted to see what the world looked like from high in the air.

185

First of all Danny stood on the sidewalk and tipped back his head to look up. The walls of the building rose straight up in row after row of gleaming windows.

"Just look, Daddy!" Danny exclaimed. "Did you ever see anything so tall?"

"This building really scrapes the sky, doesn't it?" his father said. "When you look up toward the top you can understand why people call this building a skyscraper. Come on, let's see what the world looks like from the top of the building. Let's go inside."

They went through a door into a large lobby shaped like a triangle. Along one wall was a row of doors. These were doors to elevators that carried people up to the offices above. Danny and his father took an elevator to the top floor.

"Will your elevator go fast?" Danny asked the operator as they sped upward.

"It'll go a thousand feet a minute," the young man replied.

"A thousand feet!" cried Danny. "How tall is this building anyway?"

"Seventy-seven stories," replied the operator. "That's a little over a thousand feet."

"My goodness!" Danny was silent for a moment, taking this in. "I used to think our church at home was tall."

"This was the tallest building in the world when it was built," said the operator. "There's still only one building in the world that is taller. Mr. Chrysler's very proud of this building. He did much of the planning himself, because he wanted everything to be just so."

"I should think he would be proud of it!" Danny's father said. "It's beautiful."

Suddenly the elevator came to a stop.

"Well, here we are," said the operator. "Top of the building."

"The *very top?*" Danny asked.

"Well, no. There's a tall spire above us, but this is as high as you can go."

Danny and his father stepped out of the elevator. A handsome dark-haired man was standing at one of the windows. Danny and his father went to one of the others.

His first glimpse of the view before him took Danny's breath away. Near by other tall buildings soared gracefully into the sky. Far to the east, beyond the city, lay the ocean. To the west was a river, its banks lined with piers and ships. Beyond the river the land stretched away as far as the eye could see.

"Golly, Daddy, you can see a long way, can't you?" Danny exclaimed.

"Yes, indeed," his father said. "That land across the river must be New Jersey."

"I wonder how far we can see?" Danny asked.

"I don't know," his father replied. "I wish I

188

did. Do you know, sir?" He turned to the dark-haired man who was still standing close by.

The stranger smiled. "Yes," he said in a friendly voice. "On a clear day you can see about fifty miles."

"Fifty miles!" Danny cried.

"That's quite a distance, isn't it?" the stranger said with a laugh. "And quite a view."

"It's a beautiful view," said Danny's father. "I think if I lived in New York I'd come here often just for the view."

"I do," the stranger replied. "I like it here. I was born in a small town in Kansas where you could see great distances over the plains. I like that feeling of distance, of space. I like to come up here because this is one of the few places in New York where you can see so far."

"I can understand that," Danny's father said. "I think Walter Chrysler himself must feel the same way."

"Yes," said the stranger with a little smile, "I understand that he does."

At that moment the door of the elevator opened and several people came out. With a wave and a nod to Danny and his father, the dark-haired man went to the elevator.

"I'm ready to go down now," he said to the young operator.

"Yes, sir!" the operator replied. "Going right down, Mr. Chrysler."

The door slid shut, and the dark-haired man was gone.

There was a moment of silence. Then Danny said in an awed voice, "Golly, Daddy, that was Walter Chrysler himself!"

★   ★   ★

Today there is a special showcase on one floor of the Chrysler Building. In that showcase is a wooden chest filled with tools. There is a name painted on the chest, and each of the tools is marked with initials. *W. P. Chrysler,* the name reads. *W P C,* read the initials.

The tool chest is the one that Walter's old carpenter friend made for him when he was a young apprentice in Ellis, Kansas. The tools are the ones that Walter made himself.

Many persons stop to look at these tools when they visit the Chrysler Building today. For all these people the tools seem to have a message. Even though Walter Chrysler became wealthy and famous, they seem to say, he never forgot that he had started as a boy machinist.

DO YOU REMEMBER?

1. Where did Walter live as a boy?
2. What kind of work did his father do to make a living for the family?
3. Why did his father carry a revolver when he traveled across the Kansas plains?
4. What chores did Walter do around home while he was still a small boy?
5. What did he do during the Indian scare?
6. Why did he want tools and how did he plan to get them?
7. What did his mother suggest that he might do to earn money?
8. What different things did he try to sell to people in the neighborhood?
9. What musical instruments besides the drum did he learn to play?
10. What building did he help his father put up one summer?
11. Why did he help to build a windmill?
12. What things did he make for himself while he was still a boy?
13. What was his first job on the railroad?

14. How did he get his tool chest?

15. How did he finally become an apprentice machinist in the railroad shop?

16. What important positions did he hold as he rose to success in the world?

17. How did he finally become a noted manufacturer of automobiles?

18. What large building did he have put up after he became head of an automobile company?

IMPORTANT THINGS TO LOOK UP

1. What different states could you visit by taking a trip on the Union Pacific Railroad?

2. What does G.A.R. stand for, and who were members of this famous organization?

3. Why do people celebrate Decoration Day, more often called Memorial Day?

4. Who is an apprentice workman, and how does his work differ from that of any other workman?

5. Why have Diesels taken the place of steam locomotives on nearly every railroad?

6. What different companies in the United States manufacture and sell automobiles today?

194

INTERESTING THINGS TO DO

1. Look in books and magazines for pictures of old-time locomotives and railroad cars. Then prepare an exhibit to show how trains looked when Walter Chrysler was a boy.
2. Gather information about western Kansas when Walter Chrysler was a boy and write a story telling how this part of the country has changed since he lived there.
3. Read to find out how Walter Chrysler's life was like that of Henry Ford and how it was different from that of Henry Ford.
4. Draw a picture of the first Chrysler automobile and place it on the bulletin board.

OTHER BOOKS TO READ

Early Days of Automobiles in America, The, Elizabeth Janeway. Trade Edition, Random House. School Edition, Hale.

First Book of Automobiles, Jeanne Bendick. Watts.

Henry Ford: Boy with Ideas, Hazel B. Aird and Catherine Ruddiman. Trade and School Editions, Bobbs-Merrill.

Little House on the Prairie, Laura Ingalls Wilder. Harper.

Trains, Robert Selph Henry. Bobbs-Merrill.

What Makes It Go? Rose Wyler and Gerald Ames. Whittlesey.

Wheels Across America, Terry Shannon. American Book.

WHEN WALTER CHRYSLER LIVED

1875   WALTER CHRYSLER WAS BORN.

There were 37 states in the Union.

The population of the country was about 44,500,000.

Rutherford B. Hayes was President.

1878–
1894   WALTER GREW UP IN ELLIS, KANSAS.

Bicycles were first manufactured in the United States, 1878.

Thomas Edison invented the phonograph, 1878, and the electric light bulb, 1879.

The first electric street railway in the United States was operated in Baltimore, 1885.

Henry Ford built his first gasoline engine, 1893.

| 1895–1902 | WALTER WORKED AS A MACHINIST FOR SEVERAL WESTERN RAILROADS. |

Henry Ford built his first automobile, 1896.

Guglielmo Marconi invented wireless telegraphy, 1895.

The Spanish-American War was fought, 1898.

Theodore Roosevelt became President, 1901.

| 1903–1911 | CHRYSLER BECAME A SUCCESSFUL RAILROAD MAN. |

Wilbur and Orville Wright flew the first heavier-than-air aircraft, 1903.

Henry Ford brought out the Model T, 1908.

| 1912 | CHRYSLER ENTERED THE AUTOMOBILE BUSINESS. |

Woodrow Wilson was President, 1913–1921.

The Panama Canal was completed and opened for traffic, 1914.

World War I was fought, 1914–1918.

Airplane mail service was begun, 1920.

| 1924–1940 | CHRYSLER MANAGED HIS OWN COMPANY, THE CHRYSLER CORPORATION OF AMERICA. |

Charles A. Lindbergh flew a small airplane across the Atlantic Ocean, 1927.

A great depression started in the United States, 1929–1931.

Franklin D. Roosevelt was elected President, 1932.

World War II began in Europe, 1939.

1940 WALTER CHRYSLER DIED.

Franklin D. Roosevelt was President.

There were 48 states in the Union.

The population of the country was about 131,400,000.

HELP WITH WORDS

acid (ăs′ĭd) : sour substance that usually burns metals, rocks, and other hard materials

agate (ăg′ĭt) : kind of stone, sometimes used to make marbles

algebra (ăl′jê brá) : kind of mathematics taught in high school and college

apprentice (ă prĕn′tĭs) : person learning a trade

baton (bă tŏn′) : stick that a band leader uses to beat time to music

bellows (bĕl′ōz) : device used for blowing air

198

caliper (kăl′ĭ pēr) : instrument with two arms like the blades of scissors used for measuring the thickness or diameter of objects

chisel (chĭz′ 'l) : slender tool with sharp edge at one end, used for chipping wood or stone

cog: gear or a tooth on a gear or wheel

commission (kŏ mĭsh′ŭn) : money that a person earns by selling something

consequence (kŏn′sė kwĕns) : result

corps (kōr) : group of persons belonging to a special organization, as a branch of the army

correspondence course: teaching done by mail

cylinder (sĭl′ĭn dēr) : hollow object, shaped like a tin can, in which the piston of an engine moves back and forth

diameter (dī ăm′ė tēr) : the distance through the center of anything round

dignified: stately; well-behaved

foundry: factory for making heavy metal things

gauge (gāj) : tool for measuring

geometry (jė′ŏm′ė trĭ) : kind of mathematics taught in high school and college

keester (kē′stēr) : small clay marble which persons try to hit in a game of marbles

lever (lē'vẽr) : stick or rod used to pry something

machinist (må shēn'ĭst) : person trained to use special tools in making things

mechanic (mė kăn'ĭk) : person who repairs such things as locomotives, automobiles, and trucks

piston (pĭs'tŭn) : metal part that moves back and forth in a cylinder

plush: somewhat like velvet

pulley: wheel with a hollowed edge or rim

range: open country in the West, such as that used for grazing cattle

roundhouse: large circular building in a railroad yard where locomotives are repaired

spire: steeple, tall slender tower

square: instrument used by carpenters and others to make an angle like that in the letter T or L

taw: glass or agate marble which persons use as a shooter in a game of marbles

tender: small car directly back of a locomotive, used to carry coal and water

throttle (thrŏt' 'l) : lever used to increase and decrease the speed of an engine

valve: device with a movable part that controls the flow of a liquid or gas

200

Childhood

OF FAMOUS AMERICANS

CHILDHOOD
OF FAMOUS
AMERICANS
®

COLONIAL DAYS   **EARLY NATIONAL GROWTH**

JAMES OGLETHOR
MYLES STANDISH
PETER STUYVESA
POCAHONTAS, *Se*
SQUANTO, *Steven*
VIRGINIA DARE,
WILLIAM BRADF
WILLIAM PENN,

Weddle, Ethel H.

AUTHOR

Walter Chrysler

TITLE

Weddle, Ethel H.

Walter Chrysler

ach

STRUGG INDEPEN

ANTHONY WAY
BEN FRANKLIN,
BETSY ROSS, *W*
DAN MORGAN,
ETHAN ALLEN,
FRANCIS MARIC
GEORGE ROGE
GEORGE WASH
ISRAEL PUTNA
JOHN PAUL JO
MARTHA WASI
MOLLY PITCHI
NATHAN HALI
NATHANAEL G
PATRICK HEN
PAUL REVERE,
TOM JEFFERSO